The Lovers on Asphodel Way

Stephen Wade

Stephen Wade is a writer and historian. When he is not writing true crime he loves to write the kind of fiction that the market might discover, rather than write for a market that exists. So his work is quirky, and meant to raise a smile. The Lovers on Asphodel Way comes from his work as a labourer on a building site back in the 1970s when he was a student.

First published in 2022 by InkyLab Ltd.

ISBN - **978-1-9162594-5-4**

Cover design – P. Miller

For Arnie, should he ever read this

It's the summer of 1972 and the outside world is in ferment. There's a street battle in Derry and the Duke of Windsor has died. It's destined to be a summer of strikes and fights, and there's the first ever Gay Pride march. The world is in ferment.

But in West Yorkshire there are homes to be built, and love is in the air.

Will the last houses be completed by the end of August? Will the wars of the sexes never cease? Will England ever know true peace? Will there be peace in the world? And will Paddy's horse win big?

THE CAST

Paddy Lanagan, the hut man

Brenda Baker and blob (with child)

Harold and Sylvia, brother and sister

Arthur Arch, shopkeeper and ex-carer, has been on first Gay Pride march

Irene Kent, shop owner

Cynthia, student and bar staff

Andy, in love with Cynthia

Hooky Scrope, labourer

Al Hinchcliff, brickie and stand-up comic

Gordon Lightfoot, always poorly

Sime, wrestler ('The Maori Maleroa'), desperate to get Mrs Dinchop in bed

Barney Rathbone, foreman, married to Dot

Murgatroyd, ex-soldier, raconteur

Tom and Dr. Philip Stone

Ivy Carver and her sister, Joan

Mr Nigel Bentham-Caldwell

The Coach

Hello everyone. Let me introduce myself. I'm Nigel Bentham-Caldwell. I represent Yorkshire Forward Estates and the Bentham-Caldwell Group. It gives me great pleasure to speak to you today, and to put before your eyes the pride of Yorkshire building and home design. You are in for a real treat. You are about to see the domiciles of the future - the kinds of homes that the young folk long to see, waiting for them as they launch themselves on their careers and on their longed-for domestic bliss. Today, you will see not just houses and driveways. No, you will see *dreams* made substantial! Yes, Yorkshire Forward supplies the technology, the know-how, because that builds dreams!

Sit back and wait for a glimpse of the future in this great county of ours.

Thanks for the fine introduction, Mr Mayor. Now everyone, please call me Nigel as we undertake this tour of a good-sized chunk of Calderdale, and later Airedale. I'm the manager of the area for the firm, and today the aim is to show all you good people that your investments in our projects will not only be sound but will also be very forward-thinking and, dare I say it, extremely valuable for Yorkshire – and may I say that the great county of Dales and Wolds is very much in need of some cash, and some people with vision. For that is what you are, ladies and gentlemen – yes, I do see two ladies amongst us, welcome my dears – you are *visionaries*.

6

Now, down to business. The Mayor has spoken about the recently completed suburbs of Lunderworth and Spital Valley. These are the pride and joy of our great enterprise here, which covers a stretch from Halifax over to beyond Haworth - of the Brontës, of course - and across almost to Ferrybridge. Now, as our wonderful driver, Phil, takes us slowly down this long country road towards Mirfield, I can say something about our destination for this first day of the shindig we offer. By the way, as your itinerary tells you, we stay tonight at the four-star hotel not far from Forley, The Dortington. Luxury awaits you all, let me tell you.

Right, so, we're now a mere two miles from the first branch of the three interfusing suburbs. This will be Adelphi Oaks. Completed, inhabited, gloriously traditional. Every home has a front lawn and double garage. At the rear, you might see the play area for the kiddies. When I was here last I saw a basketball net on one of the garages! Family life, you see, folks, we build for the new families of the new, ambitious Britain and its new generation.

Woah... bit of a wobble there, Phil. Hold tight everyone, You know, these roads were not made for luxury coaches. No! They were made for what my granddad used to call 'hoss and carts.' So, as I was saying, we're close now to Knotforth and in a minute or two you'll see *The Asphodels* writ large on the road-side. Oh yes. Then we shall stop at the far end of Asphodel Way, which is nearing completion, and you will actually see some homes at the very last stage of work. Our skilled people will be putting the finishing dabs to the painting jobs and smoothing over the concrete on a drive or two... So before I sit down, let me tell you what our objectives have been, from the very start.

We wanted homes that gave our new families some elbow-room, some space for the kids and some room outside to grow perhaps a few strips of veg. Maybe also enough room on the exterior for those little luxuries such as a patio - don't you love those tables and chairs for the patio? - a little taste of Spain, hey? Yes, we do. Modern young couples want room to swing maybe not a cat, but a golf club!

Now, time for a few questions. Yes I know we're stopped in a queue. That's West Yorkshire for you. Not built for motor cars - I've said that already! Oh, a hand has gone up. Yes, sir? Oh, attics. Yes, some of the new build designs have roomy attics, ready for a loft-ladder perhaps, and some boarding. Yes... thinking of your model railway, are you? Oh, I see. An extra room for kids or for Granny. Well, yes... oh, I reckon we're looking at our Montana home for the attics. Yes, well there are three. The Idaho has two bedrooms and rather a smallish lawn, deceptively spacious though... then the Wyoming has three bedrooms and more drive, more rear space... that kind of thing. Then at the top of the range we have the Montana with four bedrooms and plenty of space for two vehicles outside... oh and a side garden, ten feet there, enough for a line of *cupressus* perhaps? As you can tell, I'm not exactly green-fingered!

Schools? Oh yes, Knotforth has two schools, infant and secondary... oh within a mile of the Asphodels.

Walking distance. Pubs? Oh I wouldn't know. Ask one of our craftsmen when we do the little tour. Toilet? Well sir, Phil is pulling up right now. There's a toilet at the Knotforth Working Men's Club, around this next corner.

Half an hour everyone, to meet our site foreman and have a cuppa. Thanks. We take great pride in having our sites managed on the spot, as it were. So you'll meet Mr Lanagan. We put our trust in him.

James Joyce or What?

No, listen mate, I'm not saying that I'll not do any work. I mean, there's a tough academic year in front of us. That medieval stuff... Christ almighty. It's like a foreign language. No, no, I'm ringing just to let you know that this is the perfect chance to earn some money, save it for September... beer money in the bank and all that. What? You're working in a shop? Well, better conditions than a building site, of course but well... anyway look, why I rang you was about that camping trip with Laura and Denise. Yes, you remember. We were stone-cold sober. See, with some cash behind us, we could take them away for the week. When? Well, I don't know. Yes, it will be too cold. Yes, women like their comfort. Oh well there's another good seduction idea gone. When am I going to get some experience with women? When? I mean I've been in front of the blackboard all my life - or so it seems. *There's Andy, he's a swot.* That's what they used to say, pointing me out.

Fine. Well, a trip staying in a hotel. It would have to be a cheap hotel. Good. You find a suitable place then. Somewhere cheap. Got to go. I need my sleep. I've the sweat-work to do, and then I've to read this medieval stuff as well. Chaucer and such. This job involves some sweat-work. Cheers, Pete.

Setting up Shop

First day then, Arthur? Pleased to meet you. I'm Irene. Some call me Renee but I don't really like that. We're going to make a really good team, I can tell that just by looking at you. You're a grafter and you have a worker's hands. I've always observed people you see... should have been a detective!

Right, now then Arthur, here's where we want stuff. Knotforth folk are going to want lunches and snacks. That's the basic stock and service. Butties and buns, toasties, that kind of thing. Here we are with piles of cardboard boxes and two back rooms to fill. I've got you, thank God, for the morning bake. The way I see it, the shelves in the storeroom are for tins and such. The big biscuit tins... top shelf, and the basket trays, they can be stacked on the little wall behind the door.

Now, Arthur, would you put the kettle on please? Lovely. What time is it? Eight. Well we can open at ten today. Nine from now on though. Me? Oh I used to be a carer... nurse first of all, like you I believe. You packed it in for what? Too many mad folk... attacked you? Well I can understand that. I had one or two scary experiences myself. There was once a chap who came in carrying a sword, and he was looking for the doctor that he said opened him up and left a wooden box inside him. Totally insane. Had to be restrained by three staff.

Here? It will be just your cup of tea. You'll have a smashing time. I met one of the builders yesterday. He said they were really pleased that there was going to be a corner shop with food. They've been walking right down to the Queen's Head. Must be half a mile, poor loves! Now, we have the deliveries every Friday. You've to watch the freezer and the fridge, keep a close tag on what's running short... check on what might go off. That sort of thing. But you're the baker. Most of the other jobs are for me. As long as you keep the bread and buns coming, that's fine. The builder seemed to be a nice man. Called Barney, I recall. He was the foreman or something like that.

So you come from where? Oh, Wakefield... well that spreads all over the place. I see, this side... well you're not far off then. I suppose you go into Leeds as much as you do Wakefield? Yes, me too.

Special customers? Funny you should say that. In my shop before this, after I stopped being a home help and that, I did have a few what you might call eccentrics... *characters*. We might have a few pleasant surprises in that category. Fingers crossed. Oh, you make a grand cuppa, young Arthur. Lovely name that, a true English name. Give it five minutes and we'll set to work. You can bake first thing tomorrow, early as you like.

It could get very busy, yes. I've been told, by the previous owner, that on the next parade of shops, there's no competition for us – nothing like this. We've cornered the market, lad! Now, let's enjoy the peace while we can. Tomorrow might bring hordes of folk all hungry as wolves!

Oh, the worst thing? No doubt about it... for shop work, it's the back that gets the wear and tear. Your feet as well, of course, but the back! Oh there's nothing you can do. Hours and hours on your feet... torture. The only tip I've got is that you need to soak in a hot bath at the end of the day. We ought to have one in the back room! Shall we ask the landlord? Oh no, it's not my shop. I rent it. The landlord is very nice. Known him a long time. I looked after his mother in The Oaks. Yes, that was the last home I worked in, before I started going out on the bike and doing rounds. It got to be too much for me, you see.

So no, I'm not really the great tycoon. I just rent a corner shop, chuck. Lovely tea!

The Gaffer

End of July. End of July, come what may.

Now I've told the lot of 'em, no, no. A deadline is a deadline. No room for manoeuvre; no negotiation. There is a sign up on the edge of the road, just before the avenue and it says Asphodel Way, and that means a *place*. A place, not a vague notion. After all, I'm the foreman and the foreman is the boss and although I'm only five feet and a matchstick I'm in charge. The problem has been the rain. The rain has soaked everything from stray dogs to the ham sandwiches. Nowhere on earth can piss it down like Yorkshire. What did the benighted county do wrong, that it was so pissed upon by the Almighty? But no, it's not the Almighty, it's Murphy, the weather deity, brother to Gridlock, the traffic god. So anyway, as a good Catholic I know that patience is required in this life but for heaven's sake, no more bloody rain, please.

Rain means the buggers stay in the hut or run to the club. Rain means they play cards, tell smutty jokes, tease Gordon about his digestive antics and then adjourn to the WMC. The damned Knotforth Working Men's Club. What a firking irony! There *are* no working men in Knotforth. No, by God, they're all crocked. Rightly is it called Knotforth, all tied up in the past, like some spider has spun a web and is throttling the sense out of them.

But they *will* work. They will. A deadline cometh. I told the Big Man July and July it will be if I have to bust a gut and develop a hernia. I've built churches, holy places. I've built office blocks to house thousands. I've built bridges. There are military fortifications in the former Commonwealth nations which have been built by Barney Rathbone and his shovel-toting minions. But I mean for Christ's sake – and now I'm blaspheming mind you – these men are not building men! No, I'm given amateurs, layabouts, shirkers, gurriers, con-artists, mountebanks, crooks. I've a man who can't lift a brick without a twinge in his trossachs. I've a man so ruled by the feminine in his house that he whines about cold chips or mucky chairs in the hut. I mean, I've a right shower under me. A shower in the bloody rain! What a laugh!

I'll be having nightmares about the bloody Yorkshire rain and that bloody Working Men's Club.

But we will meet that deadline. I'll get on their backs. I'll crowd them so they shiver with fear. I'll haunt the buggers. This is 1972 and the world needs houses. There will be a million places like Asphodel Way, sure, but not made with the skill and craft of a Barney Rathbone gang.

I look inside myself and what I see is a man honed and chiselled by hard graft. I see a man whittled out of pain and suffering, chipped and pointed from the very stuff of misery, brought up in the ground floor of a back-to-back slum with a midden half a mile away. I look inside me and I see the product of that deprivation. Course, you would never breathe a word of that to this riff-raff.

Look at me, sitting here by myself, nibbling a cheese butty and looking for all the world like a polite, sensible boss. Fact is, if we can't get the Asphodels up and running by the end of summer I'm stuffed. But we'll do it.

What do you say, Al? What's wrong with the bricks? No engineers' bricks? There must be. I ordered three thou. Check again. Oh that bloody phone....Hello, Barney Rathbone speaking. Dot... is everything alright love? The what? The fence... oh, that dog's getting in again! Right... yes I know, I do everyone else's jobs but your house goes to rack and ruin. You've said that before love... Look, I'll see to it tonight. No, the job is not too big. I had it all sussed before I started. I've done bigger jobs than this... remember Birmingham? Right, well just leave it all to me and you look after yourself. Yes, I will remember the fish and chips.

Think about that holiday. Think about us on the beach. Ice creams, sun tans, taking time to read all the papers, kissing and cuddling. Oh, think of that holiday. Yes, yes, look in the brochures. Get as many brochures as you like, my darling. You just have a good search through and find us a slice of paradise. Can you manage that? Lovely. Find something involving servants who bring drinks to the pool and where breakfast has six courses... you know the kind of place!

Love you.... yes sweety... home by eight.

Dear Mr Rathbone,

I'm writing to confirm that the agreed deadline for the building work completion at the Asphodels is the last day of July. Of course, I realise that there has been the usual inclement weather, for which West Yorkshire is notorious, and the place seems to specialise in heavy rain and glum dispositions. Now, I am writing to remind you that we were assured of your meeting that date when we last spoke.

I have no wish to become a burden. I do understand that managing a site like this, which you are making to last, finishing stages of work, is difficult with a small team, but there is a budget for additional, part-time workers, and so we expect you to make use of that if need be. My partners and I have every faith in you, after the splendid work at the Top Corner Badger's Wood development.

The whole board here at the company wishes to assure you that your workers will indeed receive the agreed bonus for a deadline finish. Have no hesitation in contacting myself if there are any fresh hurdles in your way. As far as I am informed, you are on course for success in this matter. A successful completion date will mean that further opportunities open up for you and your workers. I must emphasise that, as we always reward hard work and we are great believers in keeping together with successful project managers. This removes the need to begin fresh recruitment campaigns and interviews etc. There is no need to remind you exactly how much goodwill exists between your team and the company. We hold you in the highest esteem.

Nigel Bentham-Caldwell

Hooky's Opinions

Have you lot seen what's in the paper this morning? What a ruddy year! First the old Duke pops his clogs and now look at Ireland! I mean they're chucking bombs about, son against son... it's the end of the world. Paddy... what's happening to the dear old Emerald Isle? You don't know? Well if you don't know then what chance is there for the rest of us to understand? I've got Irish in my blood as well, you know. Oh yes, Flaherty from Donegal. Way back at the time of the Famine. But don't ask me to explain the madness going on now... neighbour against neighbour and brother against brother. They need to talk it all through.

Strong royalty, that's what we need. A warrior-king like in the old days. Her Majesty is all very well, but we need Henry V you know, before the battle and that. We're a tough breed. We need a tough leader. No nonsense. Good old Winston, bless the man. I miss him every day. Yes, I know he wasn't a personal friend but well, I worshipped the man. Wish we had a few of his breed around now in these troubled times... see, folk need to be told what to do. You can't leave them to be good. They're naturally lazy. How do you mean, I sound like Hitler? You talk rubbish, Sime.

The old King, well, he enjoyed a tipple a bit too much I reckon. Abused his body and that. The fact is, if they would just give me ten minutes to write what I wanted for this paper, I'd put 'em all straight and that I would. It's love. Pure and simple. Love is the answer. Love shoves hatred aside. You Irish folk need to be reminded about the Good Lord and the basics... brother loving brother... what you say, Sime? No, I'm not talking rubbish. Just because you like skelpin' folk in the damned wrestling ring, doesn't mean to say that there's good people and good intentions... what do you mean, my third marriage? Well yes, they didn't work out, but I did try. I was a perfect husband I'll have you know. What, Mary? Well she found me dull, she said that. Just because I spend time with the model planes and the Scouts. Yes, I admit she found me dull, but... okay Paddy... back to work, yes. Back to work.

The Storyteller

Listen lads, it's raining. Listen to a tale. No work today anyway. Rain. I'm your local author. You must be bored silly, so you're with the right man to grab your imaginations. This is my club. They all know me here. Yes, I'm working on my life story. Just call me Murgatroyd.

I'm calling my book *Ready for the Scrap* because I'm being bloody clever, and I don't mind showing off my wit. Double meaning do you see? Being born in dire poverty, eager to scoff a little scrag-end of chow that came my way, I could have here a species of what today a publisher type would call a misery memoir. But that is absolute rot. I was always a man up for a good old sock to the jaw of Johnny Enemy as my old Sergeant Cobbler used to say.

So it's the Club again, and here I am in ruddy Knotforth. Yes an old man in a chimney corner, looking at the women and remembering happy times. Sad end for a war hero.

The first scrapper in the family line appears to have been Ben Murgatroyd, who died around 1605, reportedly being linked to the Gunpowder Plot but nothing was ever proved and he was with Jenny Scrub at the time in Deptford, exploring her nethers. Ben was a friend of Will Shakespeare, and family stories have it that he had a hand in *Macbeth* and in *Hamlet*, as he was special adviser to the Bard on boozing. You will recall that Hamlet the Dane likes a pint or two, and that the Scottish psychopath in a kilt liked a good banquet or two, and tended to have hallucinations when in his cups. Well, that was all done so well because Ben did the research you see, checking out a few hundred taverns and beer shops, then filling in old Will with the facts of hard drinking and the perils of overdoing the dodgy bitter down in a few London dives where a man would have his backside robbed of shit balls, they were so devious and desperate down there.

In fact *devious and desperate* would sum up the Murgatroyd history.

It would have been in March, 1917 that I first met CSM Shovell and I don't regret hitting him with a baton. He bloody well deserved it because he called my Mam a whore. In fact that wee detail saved me from the firing squad and bits of good luck like that have always been part of the fabric of my life. If my attack had been unprovoked, my bones would now be under French earth, unmarked and forgotten.

Now I sit here in a warm club, still surrounded in my head by snipers in the forgotten Burmese wastelands, and I imagine I'm a ruddy General. Not bad for a Leeds lad whose beginnings were as a hairy-arsed apprentice in a carpenter's shop. By Old Nick, I'd be a Field Marshal today if the drink hadn't got me by the bollocks so young. I mean, blood and sand, in those days you passed a beer shop on the way to work as the sun popped out and then again on the way home when you struggled through the smog. At snap time you glugged more of the stuff to fight off the boredom.

But I digress, as you will discover I do frequently if you persevere listening to these military memories. Course, perhaps no blighter will find my papers and this ragamuffin life of mine will be left in the dark like a dead rat in a barrel. Notice I address 'You' – a listener. Now, since learning to put words on paper, rather late in life, being taught by a Gerry called Jurgen Shite or something, I've come to see that a writer has to pretend he knows his listener or his reader, even if the dross he produces is no more than a bagful of pile-rattling red dung. So do bear with me, you chaps, and get involved in a Yorkie scrapper's patchwork life across the globe.

I was born Schofield Legover Murgatroyd in March 1890, dropping into this vale of tears at number 33, Wellington Street, Leeds, in the green broad acres of Yorkshire. The street name guaranteed that I would have a military career, being named after the old Duke himself, something of a hero to me. The family home was in one of those tedious red-brick streets the Victorians built to dominate and repress the labouring class by means of trapping them in boxes, all lined up so that a man trying to roger his missus at number 4 could hear the farts of the old bloke at number 22 whose digestive tract was as clear and clean as a dug-out at Ypres. In fact, the chap doing the rogering was usually egged on by his neighbours at both sides, as the walls would rattle along with the old bed, and hence the chaps would stand up and shout *'Legover, good man! Good man!'* Hence my middle name, which I had to pretend was French when people asked, pronouncing it *lejover*, meaning 'the joyous one' – which of course my father was, being never happier than when his trappings down below were slapping female flesh.

We lost our Mam when I was just a scrag-end of a boy. She didn't snuff it. Oh no, she ran away with a plate-layer from Barnsley, thinking he was a cook and so would end her kitchen slavery. I only have one memory of our Mam: one day she brayed me with Dad's cricket bat for bleeding into the rabbit stew. I was shedding blood because our Fred had stuck a fork into my arm. Fred was the eldest of our nine sprigs and he ended up in Menston where they used to shut away dangerous lunatics for their own safety. He managed to write letters to our Mam from the padded cell, and Dad failed to tell him that Mam had gone, so letters kept coming, only they were signed 'Prince Louis Napoleon' because one day our Fred saw a picture of the French chappie and thought he was seeing himself in a mirror.

That was a digression. Beg pardon for an old soldier's indulgence. I should pause here because I have a terrible memory of Sergeant Massie entering our tent and bleeding all over my bully beef and peas. You see, reader, my life has been a bloody mess from the start to today. A bloody mess. A bloody tragedy. A bloody shame. A bloody disgrace. In fact, a bloody good tale now I've started it at last, aged 71 and hoping one day to land a top slot in Blighty, once my book is out, in an office with a shapely secretary and a flunky to make the tea and toast, with not a sniper or a pirate or a hill bandit in sight - just some of my enemies in the past.

Oh, Sergeant Massie croaked it by the way. Just got a letter from the Old Soldiers' Association. Poor old Massie. Fine man, fine man. I pray that when I go it will be in a scrap. I was meant to be in a scrap. Born with a caul, I had to struggle to get that off and breathe. Oh yes, always ready for a fight, I am.

At this point we must return to CSM Shovell and my part in the third battle of Verdun. I shouldn't have been there really, as the Frenchies were plugging the hole, but I had spent a few hours with a *Madame,* whacking away with old Spadger, and as I cried out *'Mercy me...'* in the throes of fornication I was carted off with *Numero Trois* division to the Front before you could say *zut alors.*

Mine's a pint of bitter if you're going to the bar, mate.

Veg Patch

A man could be self-sufficient here, Barney. No, I know it's not really allowed. I know that. Yes, I know it's just a hut, but listen, listen. I've been thinking. There's a fair bit of land around this hut, right? Yes, right. So, I've done some measuring and I've drawn this plan... see. Top corner, behind the concrete bags, a frame for garden peas and some of them pinkish long beans. Far side, spuds, Maris Piper; left hand fringe, cabbages and nets to keep the bugs off. Then, to crown it all, in the centre by the gate, rhubarb! There is nothing like rhubarb, Barney. It grows virtually all year round. You need do nothing but slice it off when it's ready... then a rhubarb crumble with custard and you're in heaven. But wait for it... there is something else. See that few square feet by the shovels? Cucumber, Barney. Cucumber. Known around these parts as *buy it, peel it and chuck it.*

Now, self-sufficiency, that's the latest craze, right? See all the new books about grow your own? Well we can add to the national production targets by making this plot a right vegetable empire. What do you say? The latest thing is goats. Everybody is buying goats. There's enough room out there for a goat, surely. No, they're no trouble. You tether the billy and you let him loose at the right time. Then there's the nanny, and she'll have lots of milk. Very good for the blood, this goat's milk.

No, it's not strictly part of the remit, I'll admit that. But we're wasting valuable land. You know like in the war when they wanted everybody to grow their own... and there were rations and such? Well... I know it's not wartime. I'm just... well, yes I'll cover it all over if the inspectors come. Leave that to me, boss. How about that? No? Well could you maybe think about it? Just think about it... as a possibility I mean.

f.a.o. Mr Harold Mond,

No.1 Asphodel Avenue

Knotworth

Dear Harold,

It is so long since I wrote to you. I suppose it is really. Here I am in Australia and there you are back home. Anyway, I'm writing to say something when in fact words do not exist to explain what you must be feeling. Your Bessie will be much missed. She was a wonderful woman, full of love. I shall never forget working with her in Korea when she was the heart and Seoul of the W.V.S. That was her joke, by the way.

Much love,

Sylvia Gledhill.

Oh Sylvia! She writes a lovely letter. I'll have to get sorted out. I've let everything slip. Crammed behind the clock is that dratted electricity bill... and a bank statement. Still in their envelopes, unopened since they arrived a month ago. I spend my days playing chess with myself as opponent. I always win, but the only word I spoke for a week after the funeral was *checkmate!* I'll have to get myself back on track. I mean, I spent hours just staring into space. Then I might move the ornaments on the mantelpiece so that they're in line... put a picture straight... make some tea. Look into space again. Get a grip, Harold. Talking to yourself again. Is it some kind of illness, I wonder, talking to your reflection in the bathroom mirror?

Piss it Down, Please

I don't know why I've called in at Knotforth Parish Church. Just passing, called in.

A man has to have a reason to call in, I guess. Sorry to say but I'm a wandering lost soul. Oh yes. Lapsed. I'm so lapsed I've fallen over the edge. Old Nick has his sights on me, Lord.

I know we've had two dry days, after a hell of a lot of rain. That's my reason for this little plea. The dry days are the problem, boss.

Look, I've never been one for God. I mean, if you are up there, then well, I'm sorry I've ignored you for so long. I'm known as Sime, but properly I'm Simon. Now, I recall from Sunday School that you had a mate called Simon so... well, I'm not sure why I said that but I did and so, you see, now you know what kind of a bloke you're dealing with. All I'm asking is some rain. Why? Well you see I've got a sore head and a back that is about to collapse, and all the bits of my spine tip out and spill across the hut floor. So, if it pisses it down, we'll have to go to the Club and so I'll be fine after sinking a few pints, and so tomorrow I'll be ready to graft again.

Now, see, there is another reason, and it's to do with women. Specifically, it's to do with a certain married lady. Now she works behind the counter at the fish and chip shop, part-time, and she will be there this afternoon from four... see, this is right next to the Club, and you see, she fancies me, I know that and... well, need I say more? Just a good old sheet of rain, like Yorkshire does so well.

That's all I ask, Lord. I'm not asking for a flood so that we'll need Noah and his skills with a hammer and nails. No, not that. Maybe five hours of rain, in buckets, in steady, non-stop, hair-flattening, skin-soaking water. Enough to trouble an otter. That would do reet well.

Then I can spend some time with some ale, and come four, I can spend an hour buying fish and chips and rattling out the old patter to that grand little lass with the brown hair and the shiny eyes, and oh, that beautiful... oh, I'm sorry, I forgot I was praying... I mean, I suppose this kind of talk is not suitable to speaking to the Mighty One up there. I'm nothing more than a working man you see. I missed school – apart from the Methodists when I was little. I missed the education I should have had you see. So talking to the Lord is not something I'm good at.

This is a great new piece of wonderful female as well. Married. What a corker! She really *is* something! Everybody says settle down, find the right kind of wifely type, think about family and that. What I say to that is *maybe*. Maybe rainbows might be made of steel and mountains get up and walk. Maybe.

I never ask for much, now do I? I only want water. Lots of water.

So, to sum up, if you could see your way to providing enough water to soak a battleship between now and four, then I'd be happy as a pig in muck.

Amen, old pal.

Hooky on Campaign

By that was a grand bacon butty that was. Andy, tell that lady at the corner shop she's *cordon bleu*, she is. *Cordon bleu*. That's French. I'm not just a thick plasterer you know. I've got certificates. Yes, very funny, Sime, I should be certified... very funny I'm sure. You're such a wit. Look, old mate, can you speak three languages? No. Well I can. I've worked in Germany and in the Middle East. I've picked up languages and more skills than you've had hot dinners. I tell you something else as well, you were going on about love, as I was saying t'other day. Well, I didn't mean sex. With you it's all sex, pal. You spray it about like kitchen-cleaner fluid. No, I'm talking love, the kind that means caring for folk.

Love is the way forward. Love. Read the papers and what have you? Blood and hatred. Neighbour against neighbour. It just won't do. We need a strong hand at the helm. Like Stalin. See, you might look at his record and tut... but he was doing tough love. That's a fact. *Tough love*.

No, I'm not aiming to be a bloody vicar. It's plain common sense. Look at all the trouble in the world. Disgraceful! There's India and Pakistan fighting... then there was that plane crash... over a hundred dead, in London. No, I know that's nobody's fault, but it's all modern rubbish isn't it? I mean if we stayed as we were in say 1900 there would have still been enough love around. The big wars killed it all off. Am I right, Paddy? Right, back to work, I know. You don't have to speak. I can read it in your face, man! I'm just saying that the two gert big wars, they killed off something. They rubbed out too much love. It was all hate and cruelty. Folk forgot the basics... care for each other... no, don't you call me creeping ruddy Jesus, Simon... I'll ruddy well chin you! Sorry, Paddy, sorry. Yes, I'll be off to do number ten's kitchen. Just tell him to lay off me will you?

Gordon

There *is* something wrong with me. There we are - I said the words. To myself that is. Now I need to say it to them. They don't know what it's like to have a chronic condition. No idea. It's so bad I've started talking to mesen. I suppose they all think I'm doolally. Well, now I have proof. I have this condition. It has a name, though I've forgotten it now. I'll have to look it up.

I know that this time it's serious. I feel it. I *sense* it.

There has *always* been something amiss. I was *never* right. Even as a baby being dandled on mother's knee, there was something wrong. There was the crick in my neck. That was not normal. Not at all. Then there were my lungs Like a paper bag, one quack said. *He's got lungs like a paper bag and you must treat him with great care.*

Walking up the road, after delicately stepping down from the platform on the bus, I feel the words running through my head. The lads will want to know. They will want to know if this time, I had the answer. I know they have a soft spot for me really, in spite of the teasing. Today I found out the truth. There *is* something wrong, and there is a remedy. They will never, ever expect to hear what I'm going to report. I mean yes, they've had it up to the chin with stories of my asthma and the rheumatism, and then of course the attack of shingles. Sime the hod-man thought that was what you found on Scarborough beach. Thick as a ploughman's butty that one.

I'm going to walk in that hut and I'm going to tell them the facts. The medical facts, regarding what is amiss with me. Oh yes. Barney thinks I've been swinging the leg. Yes, but now he'll be put straight. There I was in the surgery, being put through every test known to man or beast. They checked my pulse, my heart, my eyesight, my hearing... I've always had lugs what stick out and I asked the quack, I said, why do they stick out? He said, so they can hear round corners. Clever man, that quack. Got degrees from Edinburgh. Oh yes, can't beat a Scot for medical matters.

The truth is, I've been a shadow of a man, walking around, suffering and just forcing on a smile when pushed. When pushed - that's what life has been like. That lot bloody push me, you bet they do.

I shall walk in there and tell them all. I can see it now - they'll choke over their mugs of tea when I tell them what he said. He's a professor. He's got brains bigger than the whole hut put together. Everything I've suspected over the years, it's true. There's a basic flaw in me. It's like a vein of sickness marked right through a rock. And somebody actually saw it and gave it a name. I can't recall what the name was, mind. But I know the result. I know the diagnosis... and the cure! Thank you God!

That is the best way - to walk in and come out with it. No fear. No collywobbles. They will understand. They are pals, when all said and done. They have the humanity to help a sick and ailing workmate.

No they don't. Who am I kidding? They laugh. But there we are. You have to be a man in this life – face the cabbage-heads. Be better than they are, laughing at a man with ailments.

The Hod

I had twenty bricks on it yesterday. The young lad was dazzled. I have to say I'm up that ladder and on the planks like a bloody gazelle. But a gazelle can't lift twenty bricks. It's all about keeping toned, keeping the muscles right. You know, flexible. I'm on the small side for a wrestler, but I've beaten bigger men this year. I beat Chief Red Hair and Lumberjack Les this year already. For eleven stone eight I don't do bad. Course this lot don't know who I am. They know I fight, like. But I don't say much about it. They don't know about The Maori Maleroa. Warpaint, dance, mad face, all that. That's me you see, that's my stage-name. I'm a showman. Oh no, I've not got any Maori blood... by heck lad, it's not serious. No, I don't think the actual Maoris will be offended... will they? I mean, what about Fred Hatherbridge up in Hartlepool? He's the Sioux Slammer. Will the tribes from America come after him? It's show business, lad, show business!

One day – the day will come – the Maori Maleroa will be famous. He will win a major title. It's just a case of dedication. You have to master the routine, every day, work all the time, to be famous. I mean, I can see the Maori Maleroa on telly. Oh yes, he'll take on the best. When he's famous, he'll have a massive villa down in Surrey or somewhere posh like that, and they'll make films about him going back to his roots and having a pint with the lads in Wigglewood where he was brought up like. Oh yes, the day will come. I can see it now - mug shots of Maleroa, close up, proud as a new mam. Then a sequence of shots of him running out doing his training, and a voice-over something like *The Maori Maleroa does ten miles a day every day of the year... he runs in snow and ice and he runs in the heat of summer... tough as leather is this man from the southern hemisphere...*

Today though, twenty two in the hod. Now then Andy, give us a push... yes, I'm off up there. Twenty two today. Watch this, young fella. Then you try it with six. You can do six. Something to tell your mates at that fancy college.

My dad gave me this hod – left it to me I mean. He worked on some big hotels in Leeds and Bradford. Could lay twenty bricks a minute with his eyes closed. This hod, see it's got his name on it. Bernard he was called. Known as Bernie Earnie as he worked day and night to see his family doing well. Now, I was told that this hod was made in 1803 when Napoleon was making plans to invade Old England, and walls were needed. You see the trims, in steel? I put them on. Otherwise it's pine, reinforced with strips of tough thick oak. My dad adapted it for his own work.

Life is all about the right tools – in every way I mean. But, no I'm not being smutty. It's a fact. Look at my tools for instance – the brickie's gear, trowels, mortar and a dash of spit. But the hod is the main event. *The hod.*

Try it, Andy, feel its strength. Good... yes, you've got a good hold there. I think you could be a brickie if you didn't want to be a brainbox. What are you studying to be then? A writer? Wow! What kind of books? Mucky books make the best money don't they? I can't see you writing

mucky books. You act like you're the vicar's lad. Coming
Paddy, coming... see you later.

Family History

Sit down lads... mine's a pint of bitter. Rain today. You can't do any work on that site. This is the place to come. This is a haven. You come here to escape the wives, right? You come to avoid work, also right? Of course I am. Trust your mate Murgatroyd.

But first to return to my family origins and early life: my father has not been introduced properly. He was far more than a bed-presser and a lover of the ladies. Devotion Getonboy Murgatroyd was from a Quaker background, but he had disgraced himself by being caught pleasuring his member in a pew during a dull sermon at a special festival involving two cups of tea rather than the usual one, and a performance of *Steadfast in the Lord's Grip* with one permitted smile per chorus.

Pull up a chair, lads. Pull up a chair. Mine's a pint of bitter.

As he grew to maturity, *Devotion* was dropped to the short form of 'Dev' and the world in general took this to mean Devil, based on his outrageous behaviour at school and later in the intended probationary period of training to be an illustrator at the renowned pottery in Leeds. Dev was skilled at losing his position. After a dinner break of four pints of ale with whisky chasers he returned to his seat and destroyed 200 fruit bowls, a dinner service intended for Lord Shute and a cornucopia with bower birds. He was dragged out screaming and the beginning of all our woes as a family was in that disgrace.

He was in the third day of a new occupation cleaning windows, not long after marrying our Foster-Mam. He started out in the trade as a wringer-out to a one-armed window cleaner, then graduated to using the wet cloth with mucky water and spit. The future seemed reasonably bright because he was nifty with a bucket and cloth, but once again Fate stepped in and he slipped, plunged through a window at a milliner's in Boar Lane and filled a dozen hats with shards of glass, while also breaking both arms.

It was the months of spoon-feeding and arse-wiping that finally did for our Foster-Mam. I always felt that humiliation was the germ of her discontent. We sprigs, chewing on dry bread at the massive table with only three legs often heard Dad's calls from the outside privy, *'Missed the pot, Bessy... wipe again!'* No woman should have to endure that. I wouldn't ask my batman to do that, though he has pressed my piles back in on a few occasions.

Back to the action. We were expecting the next Big Push and my batman was peeing himself. There had been Big Push talk for three months and all we had were a few snipers, and that introduces one of my worst memories of the Big One. I'll tell you about that, but then I must press on to my imperial theme – the face-off with the Bosch at Carie de Berges and the comeuppance of Shovell.

Now, the sniper – I was a little too bold this time; after taking a peep over the parapet I was sure all was clear and walked briskly along the trench with a whistle and a song. My aim was to taunt the buggers. To cap it, I swing Spadger in the air and of course the thing expanded somewhat with the centrifugal force. Gerry must have thought it was a chicken or something and he shot at it. Now, a spadger with a hole in it is bad news. The *Madames* check you out before there is any jig-jig allowed. There's a bulky big Frenchie on the door, solid as a bull, in case poor Tommy makes a stir of course.

Spadger was manufactured by the best spunkus interruptus firm in the land, with best rubber to fit the member good and tight, but it couldn't stop a bullet. They had never been known to snap in moments of *oh ye Gods that'll do Miss* but a plug of lead cracks the whole John Company. The men were in fits at my dilemma of course, and I could hardly borrow another. This worried me for some time, as I had - and still have - the *call* once a week, normally on Thursday afternoon after beef.

I have no idea why I was rebuffed and scorned by my peers at school but so it was, and that's rather good training for the army life. At games I excelled at avoiding any participation, the reason being that all school physical exercise was focused on torture. The regime was meant to produce grafters at the great wheel of Empire, either pushing a pen or digging a hole, shooting the restless hordes or shifting weighty items of killing machines from A to B. I was destined to be a reject when young: my brain capacity was that of a flea, my stamina that of a sloth and my speed that of a grossly overweight pig. All this meant that rather than go into a mill or on a farm I was sent to join the ranks of the Poor Bloody Infantry.

Now I have never been one to show off, but it has to be said that I am one of a rare breed: those few rare bods who journey from squaddie to officer class. That means I rank with men such as Bill Robertson - a dear friend, and oh how I recall hunting for boars in the wilds of the Punjab - a man who started as a nobody and was Field Marshal in the Big One. My progress as I tell you this has been to the rank of Colonel, and I haven't finished yet. Today I could have been a Field Marshal if it wasn't for Beefy Cottrell and that business with his daughter. I was never in her room and I was never anywhere near her person when she was allegedly touched and interfered with. Course, in the army word is spread like the clap in Gay Paree and heads turned, whispers were whispered and Cottrell saw to it that I would stay below tops in the pips league. Course, he retired three months after the first Ypres, and I laid schemes and strategies.

But back to school, and then I'll move on to the Big One. Blood and sand! I hated that monster Mr Gethin Pryce-Jones – a double name for a double bastard I'd say. Until he came the school was quite content to have form sprints and touch rugger with a felt cap. Oh no, that wouldn't do for old Taffy Shitkins. No, he was out to make an impact, mostly on buttocks and ballocks. He cracked a few egos as well and oh if he had only brought down Beefy Cottrell I would not be in the mess I am today. Nice pun what? Yes he is, if I may say so without risk of a libel suit, a haughty, slack-arsed, pock-faced, bent-nosed, bow-legged, illegitimate festering alimentary canal passing for a British officer.

Mine's a pint of bitter, lads.

End of July

Done by the end of July. That's the target. I'm standing here, staring out at piles of sand and grit, and split bags of bloody mortar, and what I see makes me think of chaos. I'm here, in charge of chaos. But I have to keep saying to myself, end of July. All this, by that date, will have been transmogrified from heaps of crap to a wonderful sweeping, majestic estate of beautiful, well-appointed family homes. I'm standing here saying to myself, asphodel. *Asphodel.* The word is beautiful as well as the place. You know, Barney, you are looking at the Yorkshire of the future. When you're an old git down the pub nursing a weak pint, you can smile at the thought that you played a major part in building Asphodel Way, Asphodel Avenue and Asphodel Crescent. I'm going to have a plaque on my kitchen wall with 'Asphodel' on it, and a picture of a wonderful semi-detached with a swanky big garage nudging up to it. Yes, yes, Barney, have another whisky, treat yourself. No bugger else will. End of July. Oh heck, better ring home.

Think of that day, years ahead, when you say, proudly, that you played a part in making these homes happen for the young mothers and the little chisellers. Think on that, my boys! Isn't that what you call them Paddy - chisellers? Yes, I'm learning a bit of Irish.

It will soon come. The days bounce by like the kid's ball in the backyard. I want them to be long and slow, but they won't bloody do as they're told. They rush on, these damned days. Then before you can say a bag of concrete, there's the deadline staring at you.

About that veg garden, Paddy. Better not. I can see your point. But no, because it could lead to big trouble for us, mate.

The March

Two potted meat was it, Andy? Right. Yes, four cream buns. Oh it's true, I was there... at the first gay march. 1970 it was. Highbury Fields. There were not many of us. Less than two hundred. There were the usual cement-heads shouting at us, but there was enough noise coming from us to make sure we were noticed. I'll be there next week, first of the month. I'll be there, proud.

Yes, wonderful. You know, the day will come when we can love anyone we want to and no porridge-head will abuse us. It's true... yes, I've had dung thrown at me. I've had men spit at me, right in the face. I've had a bloke one time swing a golf club at me and it cracked me across the back. No potted meat left. Will Spam do? Does Gordon like Spam? Right. Spam it is. No, you see Andy, the young people, like you, they will change things. It's been a long road to where we are now... legally I mean. I know a man, he's fifty. He was beaten nearly to death in Halifax when he was young. He was holding hands with his lover. They were chased by a gang and thrashed. He only survived because two women arrived and the gang ran off. Yes, your generation, Andy, you will bring the light. Shine that light into the darkness of prejudice, chuck.

You do? You know a gay student? Well you make sure he's not sent to Coventry. Treat him just as if he was normal. You know, I don't care if a person has blue skin and wears plastic bags....they are human and we let them live. It's as plain as that. Any crisps?

Yes, cheese and onion for Simon. Is he still being hunted then? I heard there were people looking for him. What's he done now? The Maori Maleroa been too rough, has he? Women? Women are after him? That's what he wants, isn't it? Oh, husbands. I see. Surely it's time he chose single friends, not married ones. Still, he has that sparkle. Life, Andy, the man has life. I respect that. He's not dead upstairs. There are enough cabbage-heads around as it is.

See you tomorrow, chuck.

Second Attempt

I've called in to have a chat again, Lord. Look, I don't ask for much do I? It's Sime again. I mean, generally in the past I've left you alone. It's not my style to nag. But if you could see your way to sloshing it down tomorrow, I'd be a Christian till Judgement Day. Course, I once was a believer. You know that. I lapsed. I'm weak. I lapse when there are pretty women. In fact, now I come to think of it, you're always putting pretty women in my path. It must have been the war. There was a shortage of men, and maybe there still is. Only a few decades back they were being slaughtered. But could you perhaps put a few more of these attractive sirens away from my line of view please?

Just keep Denise in my path, will you, Lord? Also make it rain. A good, solid Yorkshire sluice-down would fill the bill. Enough to keep the work away and give me some time to show the woman how I feel. I promise that, if you'll just drop a considerable shower on us, one to last all day, then I'll come back and make an offering. I'll give something to charity. My old train set! I'll give my train set to charity if you'll make it piss down tomorrow? Deal?

In fact, come to think of it, I like this little church. I love the carvings. I think this was all done by monks. Yorkshire monks like Brother Sidebottom and Brother Hubbleslack. Well Brother Sime will do a bit of his own if you'll only grant this one little prayer. I'm very handy with bricks and mortar, Lord. I'll do some pointing on the back wall. Promise.

'Bye for now, old mate.

The Book of Love

Poems. You see her and you have poems rising up in you like that lovely feeling you have of warm porridge on a freezing cold day. No, that's crap. That's not a poem. Get a grip, Andy lad. I never thought I'd have images of her invading me like a germ in the blood... I mean a good germ. It's a good thing, her being there you see. The fever in the love songs is true. Cynthia is like a fever but a nice one. I mean, she could be a *girlfriend*. I love that word. You can walk out and you can hold hands, and you have a girlfriend. Maybe you'll kiss. But I haven't asked her out yet. I don't know where to take her. *Woke up this morning feeling fine... there's something special on my mind....*

Thing is, I feel a shiver just seeing her in my mind. She's like an Italian. She could be Gina Lolla whatsername. I've *got* to speak to her. I mean more than *'A pint of mild please.'* When she turns around, to take something off the shelf behind the bar, I see the shape of her body. There's her little soft neck as well. She's perfection. But how do I do it... I mean, speak. What do I say? I've seen men chatting women up. They dive in, talk gibberish, but they raise a smile. Cynthia never smiles. She's not happy in that club. It's a crap place for a beautiful girl. So what do I say? Talk about the weather? People generally have no idea how the sexes break the ice and speak for the first time. We don't learn it at school.

I'm going to make this pact with myself. Before the end of next week, I'll ask her out. I'll offer to take her to the pictures. I think she's a student like me. Christ! Just think of speaking to her. I feel weak. I lose all sense of reality. I lose the certainty that I'm Andrew Layne. Women have such power. Do they know that they do? What would she think if she knew that I still read *The Hotspur* and I'm a fan of Red Star Robinson? She's a student as well. We have souls alike, we want the same things. She's so beautiful. Sometimes, in the club, I spent hours just sneaking looks at her arms. Delicate. That's what they are. Delicate. Feminine. I could just kiss them all day.

She might think I'm a creep. She might think I'm shady. In fact, come to think of it, how does a man make a woman see that he's not lusting after her body? Well, I suppose I am, but that's not the main thing. I mean, I love every word she says. I love all her movements. What's that line from the poem? *She makes all her bends adorning.* Who wrote that? It's Cynthia, anyway. Every move she does, it's just... well, it's alluring, that's what.

Cynthia, oh Cynthia. I can't sleep for thinking about her. The long dark brown hair, and the lips! Perfect woman she is, perfect. This has to be what they say love is like. It's happening to me!

She will be able to tell, though – tell that I'm, well, truth is, I'm a virgin. I have a touch of acne as well. Typical teenager, only I'm not a teenager. Maybe she needs a more mature type. I could grow a beard. Stop talking rubbish, Andy. Women, as Mum says, like you for what you are, for your personality.

Fine. So how do you ask a woman out, then? I'll think about that.

I'll have to ring Pete. He'll know.

Racing Certainty I

Look lads, would I talk like this if I wasn't confident. I mean, how many years have you known me, Sime, and all that time I've been studying form. I can smell a winner like you get the stink of old fish. This one will win a week on Saturday – the big race at Sandown. He's a stayer and he'd stay over the course of the entire Sahara so he would. He has muscles like bricks. I saw him win at Donny last week. It was his preparation race. Now let's have your fivers, at least. Andy here will put the bet on.

You know how I'm a natural judge of horse-flesh? Right. True. I was brought up in County Galway, born in a stable with a damned great black stallion licking my chops and the braying of donkeys everywhere. The stink of horses was on me from being a toddler. When I grew up I could tell a fast nag at a distance of half a mile. I just watched 'em run, or even walk maybe, and I knew on the spot whether they were winners or hackers. Trust me, this one is a winner, and you'll want a share in the boy. He's a bay, three years old, runs like the wind. His sire was a Wokingham winner. Second as a two-year-old in the Gimcrack at York.

Look at me. You see here a man who is so close to the thoroughbreds he thinks like one. Yes, when I go up to them, they fuss me and lick me and rub their lovely heads all over my face. I've got that secret thing... you know, I sense their love for me and they sense *me*.

You know, if it wasn't for my love of the gargle I'd have been a jockey. Oh yes. Human weakness, that's what it was. When I was fifteen I weighed no more than a flea, and then the bad habits kicked in. I mixed with the wrong crowd... tinkers, gurriers, drifters, all that lot. Bad habits, that's what sunk all my hopes. I mean, yes, from being a toddler, no more than a wee chiseller, I was riding the clothes-horse and the armchair. I'd get on anything and reckon to have a whip in my hand and then I was at Aintree - in my head of course - Beecher's Brook, The Chair... here comes Paddy on his favourite nag ... striding clear. Oh yes.

But then along came the damned gargle and the lads down on the estate. Shit. It's such a shame. I have a *feel* for the nags. I do. I can stare at one, and then sense what's going on inside that beautiful equine head. Hard to explain, but there it is. True. I tried to persuade you anyway.

Look, would I spin you a line? Am I the sort of man who would tell fibs? You know I'm not. I've known most of you for *years*. Look, I'll keep writing it down on this pad of paper, write it down for you all, so that it will be imprinted in your heads. Right?

I'm Paddy Lanagan, Irishman. Racing and horses, well, they're in me blood. I was riding ponies in the womb! Ah you're laughing now, but you'll be laughing louder when you have the guts to put your money down and back this nag. This is the voice of authority you're hearing. This is the voice of a man who knows a nag from a champion. Trust is all you need: trust.

This is from the heart, a pure Irish heart of a man who has worked with the equine fraternity since he was knee-high to a chicken.

f.a.o. Mrs Ivy Carver

3, Asphodel Avenue,

Knotforth.

Dear Ivy,

Thanks for your letter last week. We're typical Leeds sisters - only happy when paddling in the sea at Filey, and that's where I am. Too bad you couldn't join Willis and me here. We're growing fat on ice cream, fish and chips, and beer.

*And by the way, yes, **knock on his door**. He'll be lonely, just like you were when the sadness got into you, chuck. I wish I could just pop around and have a chat. That would help. How we used to talk, eh Sis? Anyway, this man - knock on his door and ask if he needs any shopping done. He will be trying to be very strong, and the truth is he needs some company. Be his friend, Sis. You need company as well.*

You are going to come out here and stay with us, aren't you? It's only ninety minutes on the train, once you've got to Leeds. We could walk on the beach. There are the amusements of course. Willis could drive us out for a day onto the moors. Have a pub lunch. Come and see us, and make it soon.

I don't know how you fill your time. I know that, at our stage in life, the days are so long.

I worry about you Back next Saturday

Joan

Arthur's Pride

Oh Irene... what a day it was. I'll never forget the first day of July this year. You can see from this black eye that it didn't all go smoothly. How many? Oh I think around seven hundred they said. More were expected. The plan was to walk from Trafalgar Square to Hyde Park, and we did that, though it made me ashamed of British society, the way we were treated. I mean, some smelly teenager did this to me... just ran up and put his fist in my eye! But I carried on. I was carrying a banner, with Trev my old school-friend... it said *Gay is Good. Gay is Proud* on it. We flapped that thing around like we were setting sail. Actually, yes we were setting sail to somewhere. Freedom I hope. Freedom to be what we want to be. Some kissed you know... very brave. I was kissed, though I didn't actually kiss...Most of them ended up in jail for the night. I mean, showing your affection in public! Goodness me, whatever next? Will fathers tell sons that they love them? Will we get beyond the tap on the arm? WE took our own music, and plenty of food and drink of course. I'll never forget it. I felt scared from the start. There was a flutter in my chest as I took the first steps. My heart was rocking about like there was a tornado coming. No, I didn't wear a daft costume. I just daubed my old school blazer with *Happy gay* - but I don't know if anyone saw it because the letters got smudged. Anyway, here's this black eye to prove I was there. At least I wasn't dragged off by the fuzz. I'll remember the day for that kiss from Trev.

The Fair Lady

The husband is away. He travels. He sells lingerie. Listen, there is no guilt involved. It's fun, pure and simple. Maybe not pure...

Course I've got a roving eye. I'm a red-blooded male aren't I? What's so terrible about liking the ladies? I mean, the way they're made... oh, the curves and the bosoms and all that. I mean, they're so sweet aren't they? Now there I go, asking myself a question. And I mean, well, this estate, it's brimming over with beautiful women. How I've resisted temptation so far is a mystery to me.

I've had no luck with the lass at the chippy, so it's pastures new for me. There's a new slinky sort of woman on the horizon.

It's her from number 5, that Denise. Mrs Dinchop. Denise Dinchop. Could be a classy sort of name, that. She said she was once on the stage. Cleaning it maybe. No, shouldn't say that. I think she likes me. Saw me when I was concreting across the street, bare back and that. Some women like sweaty men. They like actors like Victor Mature and that Zorba the Greek bloke. I'm that type. She only knows I'm Sime. She heard Paddy call me Sime. I never tell 'em my full name, like. But I'm in there. Husband away all day. Bored out of her skull. A piece of a cut cake don't hurt anybody.

It's her alright. She's looking at me. You can always tell if they fancy you. It's like a sort of instinct. Going to the shops I should think, with that ruddy great dog. Looks like a bloody wolf. 'Mornin' Mrs Dinchop! Lovely day for it.'

She smiled and waved. I think she winked.

Hubris

Oh what a day! I'm ringing to let you know that I'll be late home again. No, I haven't got a bit on the side. That joke is wearing a little thin, love. No, one of the men had fallen off a ladder. Yes, Sime. How did you guess! He will insist on loading that hod too full. Thinks he's invincible. He's the wrestler, yes. Very fit. But I mean trying to hold God knows how many bricks in the hod while he shimmied up to the top planks! He's asking for trouble.

Well, yes, Paddy took him to Leeds Infirmary. Quicker than an ambulance. Could be a broken wrist and bruises everywhere. Says he'll miss the fight on Saturday. No, he always was too full of himself. The way he talks, you'd think he was Big Chief Masambula. What? You know who Big Chief Masambula is? He's one of the famous wrestlers, on telly... Saturday afternoons, you know. Your mother used to shout and swear at that one dressed like a Japanese martial arts bloke. No, Sime's not been on telly. He says one day he will, when he has a better agent. No, that's why I'm going to be late. I'm going to see him in hospital. They'll be keeping him in for observation. He hit his head you see. Sorry, I know it's a pain.

The job will be done on time. That's the top priority. When the last brick is laid, then you and me, we're off on the town, and we're off to the Med to bask in the sun... Just you and me. When that last brick is down and the last drive is concreted, it's you and me against the world, Dot.

No, I'll not be calling off for a pint. No, I promise. You know I never tell fibs, chuck. You have the fish and chips ready and I'll be there ... well, no, alright, I'll bring the fish and chips then. Yes of course. Let's say around nine. Just got a bit of paperwork to do, that's all. You know what it's like. I wish we could retire and lie next to a pool, sipping cool wine. Sound good? Sure. One day we will.

Love you.

Reminder

Look, I'm straight-talking now. This job has to be done and dusted by the end of July, or the third of August at the very latest. I've got pressure on me, lads. Pressure. You know what that can lead to. High blood-pressure. Palpitations. Night-sweats. It can drive a man to drink. I'm asking you, man to man, can we please, please have the Asphodels finally complete by that dare? Which date? Well I just said, Paddy. Yes, I said two dates, but the last date is the important one. Yes, I can spell it out. The third of August. That's the deadline. But of course, if we can do it by the last day in July then, well, the pints are on me at that awful club you go to.

See, the pressure comes down the line, all the way to me. Yes, I know you're sick of me moaning, Simon, but bosses have to do that. One day you'll have your own site and then... what? Oh, so you'll be the bloody wrestler and a big star! Well I hope you do. I hope we all see you on telly of a Saturday afternoon chucking some chubby bloke in fancy dress across the canvas, but in the meantime, you're a brickie... where's he gone? Why has he walked out?

f.a.o. Mr Harold Mond,

1, Asphodel Avenue,

Knotworth

Dear Harold,

How wonderful to hear that you have found a friend! This lady sounds to be really nice. I lived in Yorkshire long enough to know that people stand off and leave alone, keeping safely inside their little bubbles. Oh yes. So welcome this woman's friendliness. Go and have some tea with her, or ask her out, why don't you?

You were always shut up into your own little world – all the railways and the carving you used to do. Do you still carve birds from bits of flotsam and such? You are so clever with your hands, brother of mine!

People are so different here. I was walking on Coogee Beach the other day, and the joggers coming past all nodded and smiled at me. Then I met Ernest in Bronte Bay and we had a coffee and a catch-up. He's the one who loves sharks, you remember. Every time we meet I learn so much about fish and plants and, well, all nature really.

Are you going to come over? You can stay with us. Just let me know. All it will cost you is the travel. You know what a good cook I am! So anyway, this lady – Ivy – ask her out, why don't you?

I trust you haven't had another one of your episodes? I was so worried last time. If ever you feel something coming on, just pick up the phone and ring me... just let it ring three times and I'll know that I need to come and help. You don't have to say a single word. Just let it ring three times. Right, love? We don't want another episode. You remember last time... in Leeds Infirmary? It was a near do. I thought you might end up in some kind of asylum, to put it bluntly. I'm sure it would be really helpful to make some new friends. Do you have some close friends dear?

Now, one last thing. Take it all easy, one step at a time. What I mean is, never do anything to extremes. I hope you grasp what I'm saying. I think you do.

Sylvia xx

Gordon

They're at the long table, gulping down orange tea and nibbling custard creams, and here I am, walking in, looking soaked and miserable. But I'm not. I mean they all know I've been off colour again, and expect the worst. I've been attacked by every ailment in the book. If there's a wind from the steppes of Siberia, I'll get the damned bug it blows over to us. But now, see, they're all surprised, my mates in here. They will be now, I'll wager. I'm just going to say it, straight out...

The quack says there's nothing wrong with me that a bloody good shag wouldn't put right!

I've frozen them all with shock. They've stopped everything and turned into statues.

No more drugs, no more tablets. Just a damned good session to release my sexual tension, he said. Now all I need is a woman. Can any of you lads help? What about helping me, for a change. Look, have a think, and if you can come up with a suitable woman, let me know. For the time being I need to sit down with a mug of tea and a digestive. How do you mean, a doctor wouldn't say that? I heard him, with my own ears. I wouldn't tell a fib. He sat across the table and he said that there was nothing wrong with me that a night of sex with a woman wouldn't cure. Yes, Dr Smedley. You know, in Kipworth. *Young* Dr Smedley... son of the old man, Harold. Everybody knows the Smedleys.

That Courtly Love Thing

Yes, Mrs Kent, I think I love her. Cynthia. You know her - works in the club. A student like me. This is love. I know it is. We did this special unit in the first term all about the courtly love poets in the medieval times. They sort of put the beautiful women on pedestals I suppose, and served them. Served them, yes. Well it meant doing anything the woman asked. Such as jousting. That kind of thing. No, I know there's no scope for jousting around Huddersfield but a man has to improvise.

I thought I might make her a scroll. You know, a scroll with a poem on it. These scrolls, they're sort of like when there's a special memorial. They're done in stone, only this will be done on strong card. They used to be on vellum but I don't agree with that... because vellum is a calf-skin, that's why.

Anyway, basically you say how wonderful the lady is, and you write it on the scroll, and then have a messenger deliver it. I'll have it posted to the club. That should do. Myself? Well maybe you have a point. Maybe I should deliver it myself. No, I'm not dressing up as a knight, Mrs Kent!

Gordon Rings Home

Now look, brother mine, I came out with it. I just said it. I think it was a big mistake.

Paddy looked at me as if I was mad. There was a strange silence. Then Sime asked me if I was serious? *'The doctor said that? He said you need sex?'* Sime asked me.

They all chuckled then.

'I've thought that for a while, lads,' I said. *'I've thought that, well, you see, if a man doesn't let it all out, like... if you hold everything back, well that's not natural I'm sure. Wouldn't it all build up?'*

'Please! Must we have this as a topic for conversation, Gordon?' Paddy asked, pulling a face as if he was smelling pigs.

'No word of a lie...' I said, spelling it out for them, *'The quack, he said it's all I need, to put me right. A right good fuck. He didn't actually use them words, like.'*

Paddy asked, *'What words did he use then, old lad? Did he say, You need some sexual release...'*

They all chuckled again. Sime said, *'I've often thought it was an essential thing, you know. I mean. It all builds up... for a reason.'*

Paddy said, *'Yes, for to have your kids, your little chisellers, not to treat it as a medical thing!'* Paddy was disgusted.

See, they may laugh, but this was straight from the mouth of a medical man. He told me right out. He said I was what he called a frail core person. Frail core. That means that everything in my body is delicate. Actually, he said that I should be doing clerical work, pen-pushing, not lifting bags of concrete. But I said, no doc, I love the building work. It's in my blood. They all know that. What else could I do but lay bricks and plaster walls? If I didn't have dust and muck all over me, I'd feel lost. Yes, that's what he said... *a frail core*. Robust sex is the only way to have the release I need.

Go on, then, laugh, I thought. But it's true. I had seen enough of the buggers for one day. Should have stayed at home.

I decided to shut myself in the lavvy and read *The Sun*.

Racing Certainty II

I told you, get your money on. Get the old spondulix on... take it out of the bank and get it on the horse's back. It's called *Streamline* by the way. Remember that name, it'll change your lives, lads. Any more tea in the pot, young 'un? Remember the name. Now it's a clever name. The sire was River Lord and the dam was Scribbler. Good, right? The scribbler writes a line and the stream is the river, sort of? Clever. Right, you're not interested, Sime. I can see by your face. You as well, Gordon, not a gambling man. But you wait till your old mate Paddy is living in L.A. with his ugly feet dipped in a swimming pool, and ladies serving him ice creams... you wait! It will be all down to Streamline. Beautiful little bay colt.

Thanks for the tea, Andy. You're a grand lad. If I had a son... if the Lord could grant me a son, I would wish him to be like you. Brains and good manners! What a grand lad! Now I'll put a pound on for you, son, I will that.

Dear Barney,

Thankyou for your letter to the office concerning the necessity of extending the deadline for the completion of the Asphodels work. This is most disappointing, of course, but I have persuaded the board to accept this, as there appears to be no course but acceptance. As you explain, this has been due to the weather and to the illness of some members of your squad. I understand that one person in particular is dogged by illness.

Of course, we take the greatest care in considering the health and contentment of our employees; I would assume that a date around the middle of August will be acceptable? I would suggest the 15th.

My only (gentle) reminder is that sources close to Knotforth have informed me that some workers are rather too fond of the local Miners' Club. May I urge you to dissuade these men from spending too long in that place, merely because the skies turn grey? We expect the British workman to have rather more resolve and determination to see a project through to a satisfactory conclusion.

I know I can rely on you. Any further request for an extended deadline would be the cause of frowns of dissatisfaction in the faces of my board members.

Yours confidently,

Nigel Bentham-Caldwell

P.S. What happened to that report about the stolen bags of grit?

Nice Day for It

Listen to yourself, mumbling as you rest that leg. No broken bones though. Paddy says I have to take it easy, stay in the hut for a while. But I met Denise...

Nice day for it I said, with a little nod of my head... she's up for it, I know she is, that Mrs Dinchop. Oh that backside! The way she walks... shouldn't be allowed in front of a working man. *'Are you Simon?'* she asked. *'You bet,'* I said, *'you bet. Call me Sime. You must be the Denise I've heard about... they say you're a model. You are! I'm impressed. Four o'clock suit you?'*

Or, it might just rain, and then I could be up at her place well before four. The Man Up There doesn't listen to me though. I think I've led a sinful life. But I mean, knock me over with a posser, that Mrs Dinchop is just every man's idea of a woman. Like in that song, W O M A N... steady on Sime, you're talking to yourself. They already think you're barmy. Watch out, lad.

If we could just have a shower or too, then Mrs Dinchop and me, well we could have a long afternoon of love. Just the two of us. I'd loosen her sinews, by God I would. I only have to look at her, watch her legs moving, see that bottom waddling, and the little man stands to attention. Oh yes, an afternoon of love... oh there's nothing to match it: the kiss on a woman's arms, or the little bite on her shoulder – that kind of thing - nothing like it.

There's women and there's women, and then there's the special type, just crying out to be shagged. I could think of Sophia Loren but well, I have this woman right here on the estate, crying out for it.

But Mrs Dinchop, I mean to say...

She's up for it. Steady, Simon, steady boy. She wants it. She's starved of true loving. The husband is as dry as a Pennine wall and as dull as an old family dog asleep. She needs some of the Sime magic.

Brenda and her Blob

It's so nice to pop in for a chat, Mrs Kent... right, I'll call you Irene. It is nice, because well, being pregnant when you're on your own, it's very frightening. You know that. You're a Mum, I know. Just calling in here, I can ask advice you see. Still, I won't be alone for long. My Phil, he's due back from his road-work in a few weeks. We'll have money to chuck about then! Oh yes, it's very well paid, building roads. It's a motorway, down south somewhere. Anyway, my little blob, she's kicking me... A good sign, oh I know. It reminds you that they're alive and well. The nurse told me that. A quarter bag of aniseed balls please, as well as the sliced loaf. Name? Oh Arthur or Shirley... after Shirley Bassey. I think it's a girl. I've been doing all the right things, like it says in this magazine... you know, to make it a girl. Right things? Well, you tie ribbons on the bed-end and you sprinkle pink sweets across the dressing-table. Oh, and you sing songs about girls... I've been singing that Diana. You know that? *Oh please, stay by me, Diana...* Paul Anka... he looks a bit like my Phil. Same hair. Same little stutter. Oh God! Mrs Kent, you don't think she'll have a stutter do you, my little Shirley... like, from her dad? No, course it's silly. I worry all the time. How can I stop myself from worrying, Mrs Kent? Irene, sorry... Irene. Oh and a liquorice twist. I love them. Cravings isn't it? I get the preggy cravings. Oh you bet. Last week I had to have Turkish Delight. Course, I felt sick after three bars of that stuff. But I just had to have some! Oh, you're having your lunch? Right, I'll pop off then. See you tomorrow Mrs Kent.

Oh, she just kicked me again!

Is there a Mr Kent then, Mrs Kent? No? Oh I am sorry. Heart attack? Oh dear.

So sad. Yes, I will call you Irene. Or Renee. Do you mind Renee? I have an aunty called Renee. You know, when Shirley pops out and into this world, I'll let you be the aunty. I mean, there are no proper aunties. Phil, you see, he's lost his parents, and he has no brothers and sisters. They will be just the three of us when Shirley arrives... a lovely little family.

Oh yes, I'll let you get on. I can see that you're baking. Jam tarts! Oh can I order six of them please? Right. I'll be back at five for 'em. Oh... she kicked again. I felt her little legs kicking me! I'm about six weeks away, I reckon. Can't come soon enough. Phil is always away. Good money, you see. He's saving every penny. We need a proper house.

We're going to be the typical modern family, Mrs Kent. I was reading this magazine. It said that the Super Seventies were here and that everything modern was going to come along for the young workers of the land. Well, my Phil, he's a young worker of this land. Oh yes I am as well. Course. My job? Having the family of course. Oh, yes, well I will have a career I suppose. When I was twelve I wanted to be an air stewardess. I liked the uniform, and all the pilots fancying you. Perfect job for me, Mrs Kent.

Oh yes, when Shirley is grown up, I'll still go for it... but there might be a brother for her. We want a boy and a girl. Maybe two boys and a girl. I wish Mam lived nearer though. She's in Scarborough, by the sea. It's great for holidays but... well, we're going to need a babysitter aren't we?

Oh, another kick! See you later, Mrs Kent.

Mr Harold Mond,

I, Asphodel Avenue,

Knotforth,

Yorks

Harry love, how are you? Please, please would you write - or ring me, if you can. I know what you're doing. You get all involved with that train set or the toy soldiers for the battles, and you forget all about your sister Sylvia! Well, look, you mentioned that lady and I can tell that you really like her. I know you're shy.

Anyway, what would you like for your birthday, dear? Another stamp catalogue? Do you still collect the British Commonwealth? I might send you a set of the triangular ones from that African place. You mentioned that rare one, from the Cape of Good Hope wasn't it? What a perfect place to live, don't you think? Maybe we should change our street to the Street of Good Hope? Of course, you live in Asphodel Avenue, and you know what asphodel is? It's a plant from Greek mythology. I'm sure I read somewhere that it's just a fancy name for a daffodil! I think it was found in the Greek Heaven. Mr Dunwoody told me that – you know, the man who has the allotment. Now, I'd love you to ring me. You have that phone and you don't use it. I know you hate gadgets, you said that. Why don't you ask your nice neighbour to ring me for you? You wrote down the number.

I will ring you, next Tuesday after tea. Make sure you're at home, please, love.

Your loving sister

Sylvia xx

God is Good

What am I doing, Paddy? I'm pointing the church wall. No, the vicar does not know I'm doing it. I owe it to God. You're a Catholic, Paddy. You understand these things. I made a promise to the Big Man up there, and I'm fulfilling that promise. You think he did nothing special? Oh by jiminy he did! He sent rain yesterday. He sent enough rain to float the ark. Bless the man. That's a thought isn't it... who blesses God? I almost said *Bless Him*. But who does bless *Him*, Paddy? He blesses Himself? Really? You know, I'm starting to think that The Almighty is lonely.

I'm not changing the subject. Yes, I'm using the firm's materials... I'll put some cash into the jar on the table. It's only a bit of mortar... I'll be done in half an hour. It was crumbling, Paddy, crumbling. The rain? Well come on, think about it. Why would I want rain? No, I leave the green-finger stuff to you old mate. *The ladies.* Is that what you lot say about me? *He's one for the ladies?* As a matter of fact it is for a lady. Yes, *that* Denise. I think I'm falling for her, Paddy. It's serious. No, no. You can't say that. I do have a serious bone in my body and it thinks about her... no not *that* bone, you pervert! And by the way, this trowel is my own tool. It's not the firm's. Now get the kettle on. I'll be done in a few ticks.

The vicar? Oh hell, Paddy, go and divert him. Go tell him about your horse.

Goodnight Irene

Lovely to see you Andy. Butties ready. Extra tomato sauce on Paddy's. Now I was telling you about when I was a home help. True – Arthur Arch, home help and first aider. That was me!

I used to go to this old couple. Frail they were. You'd have thought a strong breeze would have flattened them. They were very old. She was thin as a brush, with matted grey hair, skin trouble. She was very ill, poor lass. He was broody, often somewhere else, dreaming like, or occupying himself with daft jobs. He was always a shadow in the background. You'd be washing up or sweeping the steps, and you'd just be aware of him, out of the corner of your eye, like.

The woman was bed-ridden. I had to turn her a lot, with my gloves on of course. The place stank to high heaven. When you stepped in the room it was urine that came at you, so to speak. It seeped everywhere. The mattress was soggy with urine the first time I went in, and I had it replaced. But by God I did some washing. I tried everything to rid the place of that smell. The whole place was awful – and I've seen some grim places in my years at this lark.

Well, this old love, she used to tell me her dreams all the time. But one particular dream she kept having, she said, and it terrified her. It was about an old lady who came to see her in the night. It started with a shadow on the lace curtain by the kitchen door, then a gentle voice said, *'For you, dearest.'* Then she'd be hit in the face and about the chest and shoulders.

She told me all this was done by an old lady with long grey hair and a bad look on her face. I put it down to too much gin. I thought she was gone, you know. Confused. She was of course. She'd lie on the sofa sometimes while I was doing the hearth and rug, and she'd mutter on as if she was a child at school again. A little girl's voice would come out of the bedclothes, when I thought she'd snoozed off. Gave me a chill, that did. *'I've cleaned the cellar mummy!'* the voice would say, in a sort of whimpering tone.

Now she kept telling me about this dream. It got nervy. I started to hate going there. Just the thought of the place made me uneasy. But one day, making the bed, I came across this grey wig, stuffed down behind the end of the bedhead. You know, he'd been wearing it – the husband – and attacking her. Laying into her in the still of night. Abused her, you know what I mean? And he always seemed so harmless, muttering to himself and offering me custard creams.

I'm so glad I switched from people to baking bread and buns. It was too much, all that worrying about folk. Now, I only have to fret about burning the puddings!

Anyway, to finish the tale... we went there in twos after that for a while. But he died very soon after. That's the worst job I've ever had to do. Her dreams came over to me for a while. Sort of invaded me like when waves come in and fill the trench you've dug in the sand.

Somebody said he used to be a solicitor's clerk, never said boo to a goose. It was just like Hitchcock.

I'm so glad I'm not in that line of work no more. So glad. Give me sandwich-making any day.

More tea, love? Oh and I've put some salt and vinegar crisps in there for Paddy. He loves salt and vinegar. See he gets them would you?

Spasms

It's no use, lads. Get the kettle on, Paddy. It's no use. I have to listen to the doctor's advice. I need that woman. Yes, I know you can't just get one, with a snap of your fingers... except for the loose ones. Simon, you're a man of the world. What do I do? Give me a list of pubs. I'm all tense. The quack, he said, *'Every inch of you is tense, Gordon... you need what the Japanese soldiers had in the war... a comfort woman.'*

'Aye... they got comfort women and my uncle got Vera Lynn! He was a Chindit.'

No need to be coarse, Simon. Anyway, I like Vera Lynn. Yes, I know what point your uncle was making. Miss Lynn was a good, moral woman. Her voice gave the sort of comfort the chaps needed. That woman in the war, she was every chap's wife, sister and mum, all rolled into one lovely, sweet personality! She was wonderful and your uncle is a brute. Was? He's dead? Oh sorry... he what? He was burnt to death... poor beggar... drunk and smoking on the sofa... oh God, it doesn't bear thinking about.

The Victoria? Thanks Simon. I'll go there and look like a gentleman. I want to attract the real sort of lady... the wifely type. Like it says in the papers... *with a view to friendship and perhaps more.* You what, Sime? Of course I want more, but I can't tell her that, can I? I can't say I'm there on my doctor's orders and I need some intimate activity... what are you all laughing at?

I hope one day one of you lot gets a spasm. A spasm is no fun. They come out of the blue and hit me like a knife blade, right down one side. I think it's the heart. It misses a beat. You'll be laughing on the other side of your face. I wouldn't wish that pain on anybody. If you had to live with this, you wouldn't even be coming in to work, I'll tell you! Go on then, bloody laugh. He's up there watching you, and writing all this down. Yes, He's up there, and He has His book, debit and credit. He's seen what you lot get up to, picking on a sick man! Just you wait! If the day comes when a spasm hits one of you, don't come to me for sympathy. I shall laugh like a hyena, like what you lot do. Philistines, you are. A man has a spasm and you just ridicule him. Disgusting!

You do know there's a place in Hell reserved for mockers and piss-takers? You do know that, lads? The day will come... as sure as Sunday's dry... when you will have a bloody spasm, and we'll see! I'll stand there and chuckle at you, when you're bent double in pain. Then see what you think about spasms. Oh yes, I knew a man once, he died of a spasm. Yes, he did. He was built like a shire horse as well, but that counts for nothing with these damned spasms...

Sime and the Loose Tile

Mrs Dinchop, I'm fine. They told me down at the hospital that I was very lucky. You were worried about me, Mrs. Dinchop? Oh, that's nice!

I've come to mend that loose tile, Mrs Dinchop. *By heck she's a full bosom that one! She's going round the back. Oh here she comes.* Yes, I've got a ladder. I'll replace it for you. Boss said you had seen him about it like. Yes, I'll have a drink when I've done... come round the back? Oh yes, I'll pop round, love.

Lovely body that one, and a lovely smile. All that time at home and bored senseless. Oh that dog, it's yapping again. It hates me. I think it's jealous. I have this feeling that if I make a move, the bloody thing will have my balls off.

She's up for it, this one. I knew it, first time I set eyes on her. Women *exude* these things. It's something animal. She's exuding now, I can feel it. I can't work properly with that exuding going on. But thing is, Sime, old lad, you're a natural at this seduction lark. Oh yes. Another conquest is in the offing, son.

Anyway, that tile: it's loose and it's dangerous. If it came down it could split somebody's skull. Up we go. *Oh, hang on, she's watching me through that bedroom window. I'm sure she's looking at my legs. Is she looking at my backside? Cheeky minx! I don't know what it is, but I've got it. She's opening the window!*

Yes Mrs Dinchop. Yes, I shall be very careful.

That dog... it's growling at me. I can see its teeth when I look down. Monster it is.

Mrs M

Pull up a chair lads. Mine's a pint of bitter. I been thinking today about my good lady... she were a little treasure. From a rubber-planting dynasty you know, sahibs and all that tosh. Well coming back from the Big Bash with the Hun I was ready to settle down. Pulls of domesticity and such. Problem was, got a dose of the Margeries down the bottom end. All down to the Frenchie ladies you see. Couldn't avoid the beauties. Problem was, how to shift the rash... and the damned itch. Oh that was hell! Worse than anything the Hun could chuck at you, believe me. There was this Indian chap, real fighter he was, bloody big blade in his turban. You know the type. Well he suggested this jelly. You rubbed it on and then, my God, it burned like the Devil's kitchen. I was reeling and shrieking all night. The other chaps in the hostel, they tried everything from whisky poured through a funnel to the clout with a cricket bat. Nothing worked. Shifted the clap, though. I resolved from that day forward to lead a better life: do the keep-fit you know, run the marathon. I was fit as a flea by the time the second big row came along with that nutter, Adolf. My sister walked out with him you know. Yes, in Southport. When he was staying in Liverpool. *'Ven vill we reach ze end of zis bloody pier, mein love?'* That's what he said to her. Never bought a round, she said, just sat there and flapped an arm when he wanted anything. No wonder he turned all Fascist.

Anyway, I met Mrs Murgatroyd and we went courting. In those days you courted the woman you see. Damned silly idea. The girl knew what you wanted and you knew that she knew what you wanted but you both talked about other things you wanted and it took months to broach the subject of hanky-panky, and even then it was a damned stupid ritual, and the women had so many layers of clothes on them you see. A man would spend a week coming up with a strategy as to how to negotiate the various garments and undergarments. Then there were buttons, studs, fasteners, clips, zips and belts on every limb and by jingo you needed a squad, all with individual skills to get anywhere near flesh!

My dear Mrs Murgatroyd was the daughter of a vicar and she had had quite enough of sermons and hell-fire threats to all sinners. Quite enough. She longed for a proper gentleman with a dash of danger in him. That was *moi.* Now you see, you young fellas, you need to be gentlemen. You need to have the aftershave, the cufflinks, the bow-tie. Charm. They love charm. Best of all, wear a fedora and smoulder. A woman seeing a chap smouldering, she'll cave in at the knees, and she's all yours.

Thanks for the pint, Simon. You're a gentleman.

Problem is, with the military life, a man makes enemies. Jealousy you see. There are people who burn with jealousy when they look at you and see that you're superior. They want to stab you in the back. They simmer with hatred. It was like that with CSM Shovell. You recall, I was going to tell you about that arch-enemy of mine? Yes. I was telling you how jealous he was. The green goddess had him by the goolies and he was after me. Oh yes! Well for over a year we were competing in every aspect of the Big Push. We caught grenades and threw them back. He matched me in that. We entertained three French ladies a night for a week... he matched me in that... so it went on. Then one day he came to me, in the dug-out and he says, *'Duel, Murgatroyd.... tomorrow morning after reveille and before grub. Pistols and bayonets!'*

What could I do? I had to agree. Of course, they were illegal... court-martial job. But one couldn't lose face, no. What? You have to get back to work? Already? Well I'll finish the tale next time. So long lads!

Chatting Up

Pete, just a quick call. I mean how do you do it - chat up women? I've seen you do it. You're a master of the seduction line. What do you mean, it doesn't usually work? I don't care, the point is you look as though you're doing well. There's this girl. She's called Cynthia. Pete – I'm not kidding. She's totally beautiful. As soon as I saw her I knew she was for me. I need to get to know her, mate.

You're never lost for words. You charm them. You do. I want a tutorial please, on what to do. I'm not being sarcastic. I got that. You don't charm them into your bed. That doesn't matter. I just want to know what works. They are alien beings, Pete! Alien beings. They function differently. What am I going to do? Yes, write me a letter if you have time. I know you're not Humphrey Bogart. I don't want to be Humphrey Bogart. Yes, be natural. I know we have to be natural. But when I'm natural I'm a goof. Fine. Yes, a letter. Write me a letter, full of wise advice. Please. You've had more girlfriends than George Best. 'Bye for now. Good luck with the translation test.

The Click

They're going to laugh, I know they are. But I'll have to tell them. I mean you can hear it, the click, if I turn to look sideways. I'll have to say something about it. They can laugh, see if I care! Sometimes I wonder if God was in a big sulk when he made me. Took his eye off the ball. Most folk, they might have one little ailment. They might have a cold. They might have a wonky finger, happen they dislocated it when young. Some are born absolutely fine except for a slight limp or a little hint of a stutter. Me? Me... I have the lot. Every malady in the quack's medical almanac. I think there are some things I've got that are not even in that book.

Then along comes this crick in my neck. Just out of the blue. I was reaching in the cupboard for a bottle of vinegar at the back, and then I turned my head when our lass called out, and *click*! It was like when you snap your fingers. I'll have to tell them. I'm going to say something at tea-break. It's one thing after another with me. Why couldn't the Lord give me a better body? It's not much to ask. I've never asked for anything before. I'm not a religious man. But just now, I could use some help from on high. If I could just feel well one day, that would be a start, Lord.

Why did the good Lord give me this body? Always something wrong with it. Why me?

They'll ask for a damned demonstration though won't they? Ask for proof. I can't announce something like that without consequences. Evidence, that's what they'll want. They'll all want to hear the actual click. When they can damn well laugh, I don't care. If a man is poorly, then he's poorly and there's nothing to be done.

Irene at the Counter

Three potted meat, two egg and cress and the usual pies. There you are love.

Now, I was saying about these institutions.

Oh, they'll have you on. They'll have every minute of your time, some of these institutions. Not long ago, when the private homes were sort of mushrooming on every street corner, there were plenty of jobs, but most were very poor. You needed nerves of steel. Fishbone in your corsets, if you get my drift.

Well, I'd noticed these places, as you do, and I'd seen a few spring up and down my way, as you do. Like I was out shopping one day and I saw that number twenty one Garrow Road – a huge Victorian place – was being converted. They seemed to be building a bit on the back which was the same size again.

Anyway, not long after, they were searching for good staff. I found myself in an office being interviewed by a man with a flowery tie bigger than my table-cloth at home. The tie, not the man. He was funny. I mean, the whole experience was bizarre. Like a twisted dream. You see, they were still plastering the hallway, and when he went out to get a file, or to shout at the workmen for playing their radio so loud, he'd come back with white patches of plaster and dust on his dark suit.

He kept saying things like, *'What sort of career move do you envisage this to be, Mrs. Kent?'*

'Well, quite good money.' I said.

He was nonplussed. *'But where do you see yourself in three years? Have you thought about NVQ?'*

I said I'd thought about the meat queue down the market. He didn't laugh. That's how it went on. I mean. You'd think the job was for directing a war strategy, not cleaning blankets and windows.

After he went out for the third time to yell at the builders, he finally admitted defeat and asked me to fill in a form while he drank some coffee and stared at the forsythia outside.

In fact, plants were the best thing about The Birches as it came to be called. But they were a mixed blessing. You see, my first day there, after it was all done and set up, sticks in my mind as a non-stop padding up and down this long hall, with old folks sat in lines at each side. It was like a great greenhouse cultivating death. There were jungle plants up the glass. You couldn't see out. The ladies and gentlemen sat facing each other across the hall you see. They couldn't look outside. I mean, there were so many creepers and cheese-plants and aspidistras or what-not. It was like a film set for *Tarzan of the Apes*.

And me? I spent six hours a day trundling a tea-trolley and emptying buckets, then maybe sweeping up biscuit crumbs and spew. First one, then another; then the relatives would call, and they'd want tea. Ever-open gobs they were. No satisfying them.

When I took my coat off at home and hung it up behind the door, our Tony asked me what the first day had been like.

'Like watering plants,' I said.

And it crossed my mind that I'd been watering for the end. I said so, and Tony turned all morbid. He could never see that I needed it all like I needed kisses. And they were always in short supply.

'You're like a mother blackbird rushing to a nest full of bloody orange beaks, all wanting something.'

Then he asked me to put the kettle on for a nice cuppa. He stared at the telly as per usual, opposite my chair. We couldn't see out.

Now I had a bit more time this morning so I've put a few special things in the bag.

Let me give you some more. You're big, strapping men and you need your strength. Proper food is essential, proper food for physical work. My dad used to say, *'Eat to avoid defeat.'*

Tell you what, have a few elephants' feet. Fresh cream in 'em. Treat for the boys in that old hut of yours. Go on, take 'em love. The chocolate éclair... that's for Paddy. He loves chocolate éclairs. Tell him Renee put that in especially for him, will you? Thanks. Actually, don't tell him, but I hate being called Renee. I'm Irene. I suppose it doesn't matter really, but Irene sounds more... more classy, don't you think, Andy? No, no, don't bother him with it. It's a small thing really. Names matter though, of course. Do you prefer Andy to Andrew? I thought you did. Much more friendly. Relaxed.

f.a.o. Mrs Ivy Carver,

No. 1 Asphodel Avenue,

Knotworth.

Dear Sis,

Yes, yes, he called over the fence because he likes you. Men are like that. I mean, yes, he only asked about rhubarb. I know you have more than enough rhubarb, but he offered some and you should have taken it, even if you don't need rhubarb. Men are like that. You should know. You lived with one long enough, girl. He's wanting some company. I mean you're a woman and he's a man. That's only natural. Just have a little conversation with him. I'm not suggesting you flirt and become a loose woman!

We came back from the seaside thoroughly relaxed. Wonderful. He was a bit burned mind, that husband of mine. It's like having a toddler again. You have to watch him every minute.

Anyway, pop round with an offer of a cuppa. Next time you're both in the garden, make a move.

We're off to Sheffield next week to see a show, but I'll write after that, and I expect a full report on Harold and your progress with him. Poor lonely man!

Joan

The Ruddy Floods

All I'm saying is that them damned floods ... the ones in South Dakota... well, they're a message to us all I think. Yes. Over two hundred decent, ordinary folk dead over there. They had done nothing to offend Him Upstairs. Nothing. What happened? Horrible great deluge in the Black Hills. I'm only Hooky the plasterer from the shit-end of nowhere, but I'll tell you this... it's a warning. Oh yes, the Almighty up there, he's seen what a mess we're making of his Garden of Eden and we're in for some trouble. He's like the Head Boy and he's mad as a stuck pig, and he's out to get us. No I am not talking bollocks, Simon bloody wrestling nutter... I'm commenting on the world's events. You never notice anything because you're attention is always on the ladies and their knockers! I've seen you. I've seen you carrying on with that married woman. Sodom and whatsit, mate.

Sorry Paddy. Yes, back to work. I'm off back to work right now. If I stayed any longer I'd swipe him one across the jowls.

Dulce Domum

Dot, I'm just ringing to let you know that I might be a bit late tonight. It's a very trying day today, and it's not two o'clock yet. You will never guess the latest development. It's the Irish man... oh what a case he is, love! This morning, I said I had to go to collect some putty. Well they thought I was going to be away for quite a while, but I came back straightaway. Now what did I see as I drove back on site, but Paddy creosoting the hut! He was up a pair of steps, pot in hand, brushing away. He says, *'Oh there you are, boss... back early!'*

'I'll give you back early!' I said. *'What the hell are you doing? It's just the site hut. It's not some bloody fancy lodge at Harewood House!'*

'It's just a lick of creosote... preservative,' he says.

'I know what preservative is, Patrick!' I said, being rattled by this time. It was then I noticed something else. You see, I don't normally pay much attention to the hut. A hut is a hut. They come and go. They are where you store tools and eat your snap. But there, on the hut, above the door , was a little fancy square of wood with some words painted on, in this old-fashioned lettering. *'What's this...* dulce domum... *Patrick?'*

'Oh,' he says, looking up at it proudly, *' I can see you never had the benefits of a Catholic education, Mr Rathbone. It's a bit of Latin, so it is.* Sweet home.

I was dumbfounded, Dot. Dumbfounded. I could have screamed in frustration. But I controlled myself and

I said that I had to remind him that we had a deadline for completing the Asphodels and that the hut was not part of the plans. I told him that the hut will be knocked apart and chucked on the lorry ready for the next job. It was not a residence for the Prince of Wales. I could tell that he was upset. He wanted to say something but thought better of it.

So, anyway, that was one little tribulation among many, but I won't bore you with anything else. I'll bring fish and chips... you get your feet up. See you soon, love.

The Lecture

Lads, lads... at this rate we're never going to do it are we? I mean we can't do anything about the pissin' rain. That's Yorkshire for you. But there are things we can do surely. Andy, Sime... you can do the internals at number twenty two. Yes? Paddy... there's no reason why you can't crack on with that guttering. You're halfway through. Young Andy, finish that trench. Gordon, show him how to mix concrete. He's here to learn, and he's being shown fuck all. Excuse my language, young man. Now yes, there's weather. But we are builders. We build. We can work in the wet, in the cold, in the heat. We're proper builders. Remember that big job in Bradford two years back, Sime? Yes, right. Sime, I see you're back. But light work only. You can't use that wrist. Paddy, put him on tea duties.

See, we have a deadline. We will meet that date at all costs. What Gordon? The Union? Well yes, I'm sick of hearing about the damned union. What? The Duke of Windsor? Oh he died, yes. No, we're not having a day of mourning. The bugger didn't want to be our king anyway. Stuff him. He died in Paris, yes. See, he didn't want to be here anyway.

There's pressure you see. I'm not the big boss. No. There's folk above me putting the pressure on. I'm the man in the middle. You understand, I know you do. It's a cruel world out there. Ireland seems to be getting itself blown up. Some think the Irish want to kill our beloved Queen! That's how bad it is. So, we are builders. We build - we don't destroy. We're the good men. We wear the white hats. What am I on about, Hooky? I'm on about the westerns. We all like a western, right? Well the baddies wear black hats and the goodies wear white hats. You see? Good.

We need to be the goodies and *build* homes for the young folk. Not blow 'em up. You get my drift? Good. Now we understand each other.

The days rattle by and we stroll on, a little job at a time. Then the hurdles appear, like in a race. The wet days, the sick workers, the nagging little problems like a delivery is late or we run short of bricks or things like that. You know what I mean. I don't have to spell it out to you blokes.

So you see lads, if we keep our eyes firmly fixed on that calendar there, by the tea-table and that soddin' whistling kettle, we'll do it. It's nearly the end of June now. We have a month. A full month. Just think of this place in the future. Asphodel Way... Asphodel Avenue, Asphodel Crescent.... it's like a poem. Now get stuck in till four. Then the pints are on me today! Right? Right.

Dear Jim,

This is the other Lanagan, dafter than yourself. But I'm missing our days out at the race, and at the fishing, in truth I am. This Yorkshire is a miserable place.

How are things back home in beautiful Galway? How I miss the big Atlantic, the damned great bully that it is. Now Jim, I'm writing for brotherly advice. You recall that about a year ago I had a sort of flirtation with a woman named Renee. Well, it's Irene really but here in Yorkshire they call Irenes Renee, to rhyme with Heaney or Feeney and other Irish names. You will recall this short-lived liaison? Well, she's making overtures again. I thought she had had enough of me. I know I can be a moody bastard and such. I know I'm subject to fits of the black dog. I thought all that had seen her off, but by God, she's keen still.

She sends me little extra treats in my lunch pack you see. She's apt to send little notes, little billets-doux as our Gerry used to call them. Oh how I wish I had been given a real university education like Gerry. All we had was the Jesuits, and by heck that was military – or worse! Anyhow, I digress.

What should I do? My feelings for the lady are still there, in a way. She's very sweet. The point is she is a carer. I mean, she used to be a nurse or a home help or something and worked in homes. Jim, what a terrible word that is. I hate the word. There's nothing homely about those places. So, in a nutshell, should I welcome her making overtures or what? I am very inexperienced with women, as you know, and this woman, she is full on, hell for leather passionate. Surely she knows what I'm like? I'll be a disappointment, Jim. I always was disappointing. You will confirm that, as a true and truthful brother. I disappointed Mary Hanagan of Athlone, you will remember, and then there was Kathleen from Gort. She thought I was more than I was.

See, I don't measure up. I fall short, brother, don't I? In the life-game I'm meaning. You know, I was born to decorate a hut, to work in a limited space. I can't rattle around the greater world of men and women without ruining somebody's ideals.

A little advice would be very nice, Jim, when you have a minute in between the milking and the rat-shooting.

Yours

Patrick.

The Victoria Episode

Well next time I want advice about the fairer sex I'll not ask any of you! The Victoria indeed! It's a knocking shop! There I was, with my Sunday best suit on, complete with my waistcoat and my dad's fob-watch. Brylcreem was slapped on my head so it shone like polished brass... and I tried a smile... I shook hands and asked a suitable lady if she wanted a drink. I'd barely finished my pint when she started fiddling with my crotch and asking if I needed some company, somewhere quiet. Well, excuse me, but I like some courting!

I was out of there as soon as you could say lady of the night, I'll tell you. The only thing for sale in there is the bloody clap! So pour me some tea, Simon, and say nowt about women.

It's that doctor's fault, telling me I had to have a comfort woman... this is bloody England. Like my dad said, when he was a Chindit fighting in Burma, *the Japs get comfort women and we get Vera Lynn...* I know I said that before but it's an important point.

Any road, brew up some tea, Paddy, there's a mate. If it wasn't for this hut I'd do meself in! She would have laughed at me anyway, laughed at the click. Aye, it's still there, only when I turn left. Don't be stupid, Andy, I have to turn left sometimes. Look, you would hate to have this damned thing, so have some sympathy will you?

No, shut up. I'll not be mocked. Shut it. There I was, innocent as a babby, thinking a lady-friend was all charm and chat. Oh how wrong can you be! Everybody stared at me. Anyhow, the damned click... I can't live with it any longer, lads. What Sime? What are you suggesting? A good hard slap on my shoulder? That should cure it you say? Not on your nellie. I'd more than likely die in the process. I have a weak clavicle. Oh, look it up, Sime, look it up. There are these things called *books*. You learn stuff in them.

The Duel

I was telling you about CSM Shovell, and the last round of our rivalry, lads... thanks for the pint of bitter. There we go, now sit down here lads. Yes, all settled? Well it was dawn the next day. There was a thick mist over No-Man's Land. Men were eating from their tin pans, and some supping whisky because we were on standby for the next wave of the Big Push. Now there was an eerie silence as I peeped up and looked over the parapet. No birds were singing. There was no wind. Across the muddy field, where nothing stirred, there he stood, CSM Wellington Shovell, tall, solid, face resolved to face death. He had Pocky Hubbard as his second, and the man was standing there, holding the pistol and bayonet. The other man with him was Bodger Copeman, who copped a bullet at Mamet Wood. Then Shovell yelled out my name.

I went slowly over the top, pistol in one hand and bayonet in the other. My mates whispered, *'Don't go, Murgatroyd... he's a maniac!'* But it was a matter of honour. A chap has to face the worst at times like that. No thought of funking it. Well I stepped out, trying to hide the fact that my legs felt like they were made of sponge. Pocky Hubbard told me to come and stand back-to-back with Shovell and I did, and I could smell the stink of his unwashed crotch as we stood there. Then we were given our command and cocked our guns. Bayonets were fixed and knives in belts. They were to be used if the bullets failed to kill.

Well yes, I felt scared of course. I was shitting myself. But we took our determined steps in the mud,

107

ready to take twenty and then turn and shoot. As I took the last step I felt my heart lurch and I thought it would burst through my khaki… but as I was about to pull the trigger there was an almighty burst of machine-gun fire and all three men fell with shrieks of pain. Pocky, Bodger and Shovell were all dead as lumps of coal, and I dived for the ground, lying flat out and then curling up like a foetus.

The Somme had begun, and there I was, pistol in hand and pants drenched with piss. That's what the thought of imminent death does to you. Sorry to be so brutal, but that's the way it was.

I'll have another pint if you like, lads, thanks.

Lost

I thought I'd ring you, Joan, and give you the bad news. He's disappeared... Harold.

Usually I can hear him moving about, you know. But it's been silent for days and days... not a sound to be heard in there. What do you think he's doing? You don't think he's.... he's put his head in the oven, do you? I mean he's so lonely. Lonely folk do things like that, if you believe what you read in the papers. No, I'm sure you're right. He's maybe just having a quiet period in between doing jobs. I'm being dramatic. But I've had a glass to the wall, I'll tell you, and I've been spying through the garden fence. He's a puzzle, that man. But nice. Men are so sulky. So moody.

I'm being silly, I know. Yes, sorry to ring up in such a panic. What? Well he could be in the cellar yes. I hadn't thought of that. He has hobbies. Maybe he has something he does down there. You're so sensible, Joan. But yes, yes, I will have a chat with him. Bye love. Yes, I promise.

The Click Again

Now, you've supped your tea and you've eaten your sandwiches. I'll have to tell you something or you're going to discover it for yourselves and then you'll only laugh and I'll get ridiculed and mercilessly teased, so I'm going to come straight out with it. I've got a click in my neck. There you are: I've said it. A click.

'A click?'

Yes Paddy. A click. If I turn left, a bit sharply, a bit suddenly like, there's this click.

'But we thought that the doctor said... oh, of course, you've not got your leg over yet of course. You can't find a woman...'

Course not. I need some time. Now see, I'll show you. I'm going to look over there towards the cupboard, like this...

'Oh yes, there was a click!'

Thank you Andy. There you go. You're all up to date with the state of my body. A harmless click. I went to the quack. He said it was harmless and would go back into place. It would maybe click for a few weeks and then go back to normal. So now you all know and there's no need for any stupid questions. Yes, Paddy? No, my head will not fall down at one side. If I only turn one way, you would never know I had the damned click.

A woman? I know he said that. But I can't just find a woman like that can I? I mean I want a proper woman, not a floosie! Anyway, I think the doctor was having me on. I don't believe it. He was out to tease me a bit. Not that I would say no if there was a comfort woman, like. You know what, I think that the National Health should have a facility where it would be called Comfort Women. You could have like a prescription... What? Oh Comfort Men as well. I'm not being sexist. No, you can have your Comfort Men. Sounds a bit strange though, Paddy, don't you think? What would they do? You could hardly have an office down the G.P's with *Comfort Man* on the door, now could you? What? You would do it, Sime? Well you would... oh, just for women. Well isn't that the same as being a gigolo? You already are a gigolo, Simon! It should say *Gigolo* on your bloody hod.

Boot-Scraper

You know, young Andrew, I was just thinking, as you sat down there and tucked into your sandwich, what this hut needs is a boot-scraper. I bet you don't even know what such a thing is? I thought not. You see, in this brave new world of technology, there are thousands upon thousands of little domestic creations which belong to a disappearing world. Oh yes, and well you see now, I'm going to take the blade of an old broken spade and I'm going to set it in concrete just outside the front door of the hut, and then before you lot of clod-hoppers come stamping in here, you scrape the soles of your boots along that blade... now that's a boot-scraper! Every home in the land used to have one, in days of yore. When were the days of yore? Well long ago... it's just an expression. No, you wouldn't be told about them in the history lessons at school. The days of yore refers to the far past... the fogs of time. Pinch that for a poem, Andrew? Well if you must. It's all my own work... the fogs of time! Good to know you're writing poems anyway. I always thought we Irish had the monopoly on poets and that you heathen English had no soul! Good for you, son!

What do you mean... woman trouble? Yes, come and talk to me any time... when it's not busy in the hut... come and tell me what's wrong. Cynthia you say, at the club? Lovely girl. I can see why you're smitten with her.

The Visitor

There's a woman looking through the window of the hut, Gordon. Does anybody know who she is? Sime, why are you hiding behind all the coats? Oh, it's Annie Baker. Oh yes, we all remember Mrs Baker, from the job at Halifax. You fell in love with her didn't you Sime? Now you don't want to see her.

'Get rid of her., Paddy. I'm behind the coats.'

Oh hello, lady. Do come in. You look familiar. Halifax? Oh yes I do recall now. No, Simon is no longer working with us. He left for America. Oh, I can see now that you're large at the front... sort of, possibly, I mean to say... with child maybe?'

'Pregnant. '

Lads, Mrs Baker has a bun in the oven! Now oh, hell see what I said! Now that's funny, and I didn't mean it, Mrs Baker. It just slipped out like. Stop sniggering, you lot. I'm awful sorry Mrs Baker... no, don't go... I'm sorry!

'She gone now?'

Come out, Sime. Coast is clear.

Neville

My Neville? Oh he's lovely, Irene. He's the perfect mate, best friend. I met him at a concert. You know I like a bit of classical? Well I was at the Town Hall and it was Beethoven's Rasumovsky. I was at the bar getting a glass of dry white when I turned and my arm bumped into another arm. It was Neville's arm. He smiled and said, *'My fault'* and *'Let me buy you another.'* He would not take no for an answer. You know what, Irene, we talked and talked... after the performance of course. During the third piece - Chopin it was – he turned and looked at me and you know... I blushed. He couldn't see of course. Subdued lighting. It turned out that he played guitar and piano! Yes, he's been to college and everything.

Oh, hi Andy... sandwiches are ready... and the buns. Three packets of crisps? Right. Yes, cash is just right. Lovely lad, that, Irene. Student you know.

Well, I think he's the one. Am I blushing again now? I think he is. You know when it's special, don't you? He's tall, thin but with some strength in him... wears a lot of bright blue and purple... he likes loud braces! Oh and hats. He has about a dozen hats. He says he's a bohemian. I had to look it up. Well he took me for a drink after the concert and we went to the Prince Albert... that posh place. You know what, Irene, he's not short of a pound or two. But money has nothing to do with it. My Neville... he's kind, gentle, has good manners, and clever... oh so clever. He's in a pub quiz team, and he's asked me along.

He has a lovely nature, my Neville. People are drawn to him, if you see what I mean. A good soul, is Nev.

Sorry, I'm going on. Yes, I'll clear up in the back. When I think of him, I lose myself. I go to pieces. Nothing gets done, Irene.

To Mr T. Stone,

Centre 223, Fair Lawns,

Nairobi,

Kenya

Dear Tom,

I'm glad that Kenya is not the ordeal one first imagined. Mother thought that the Mau Mau were still raging and that chaps with woad on their faces walked around yelling. Too much Rider Haggard. She's not too good just now, actually, but she keeps her pecker up.

We had a tussle didn't we – about the VSO. You must be sick of it. We've had some long nights going through it. Too much gin and selfishness. I know you're busy and God knows what problems you face. The insects are the worst, they say. After all, what does a provincial doctor know about the world? I know about boils and tonsils but that's about it.

Well, what's happening there? Any other whites there – Europeans I mean? Not that I'm bothered but mother is a gentle soul and she lives for knowledge. She wants despatches from a foreign correspondent and that's you! She never should have been a teacher because she puts learning before people. Maybe she should have been a librarian.

And me? I won't pretend that I don't miss you at the United game every fortnight. They're third from bottom by the way but it's early days yet and they've bought a centre-forward or striker I mean, right? I still talk about wing-halves and inside-rights. I am glad, Phil, that I developed and strengthened this place when we were younger. We are, of course, at the corner of a busy road leading to the engineering firm, but when I sit here looking out of the window all I see is our wonderful garden, my haven. The elms are exquisite and the fence, though repaired dozens of times, keeps the barbarians out.

Actually, last week some foolish youth – a skinhead type I believe – wrote something on the fence. Quite obscene. I mean, it's beyond comprehension. I don't want to sound reactionary but I see a new evil within us. I suppose you've read about this joy-riding. I mean, kids stealing cars and driving murderously around among children and old people. The new barbarity astounds me. The answer given is, 'There's nowt to do around here... see?' Frankly, I don't see. And this skinhead – well, I saw him do it. He was just giving it the finishing touches when I saw him. He put his tongue out at me and legged it.

I know you like surprises but I can't wait to tell you what I've sent. You recall that book about gliders in Brown's – it's on its way to you. I hope you have decent blasts of wind. It's only just occurred to me – perhaps you live in some awful dust-bowl. Do you have these siroccos?

Mum has sent socks and pants, by the way. I expect you sweat even if you wash on the hour. That's what I

117

found when we went to Rhodes that time. Mum's stroke has meant a lot of effort for us all but there is improvement. We ought to investigate the health-food shop. I've always been against these trendy supplements and stuff but I suppose I'm mellowing in my dotage. She's able to talk, just a little. She speaks of you all the time. In case you've been wondering since I told you all about it, then yes, she can still do quite a lot of things. I'm only needed for anything strenuous or anything involving her left arm.

Looking after her is a special kind of pleasure actually - not a chore really. Acts of love, that's what we need I think. Giving of ourselves brings a valuable, rather priceless reward. I think you see what I'm driving at.

Do drop us a line. It's quiet here – except on Saturday nights, and the ends of shifts at the works of course.

Yours,

Tom.

In Bloom

Patrick.... Patrick... hey Paddy, what are these? The yellow flowery things? What? Forsythia? They're in a little bed. Did you dig a bed here? I never saw that. We have the yellow forsythia... and, and here there's something else... what? Raspberry bushes? When did you do all this? Yes, they do make the hut look nice, Patrick. But as I said before, the hut doesn't really matter. It's not part of any great scheme of things for the damned Asphodels... excuse my language. But I get rattled because we are working to a deadline and it's approaching fast, and you're Mr Greenfingers... I mean what about the locks on number ten? You done them, like I asked? No? Well please get cracking on them now, and leave the bloody forsythia... excuse my French. They come into bloom... well of course. They *are* lovely in bloom but... yes, exactly... off you go then.

What? Oh yes, you're going to make a little bit of a *haven* here. I see the point but... a haven. Somewhere you can think of as home, just somewhere to gather your thoughts, rest your aching feet... have a cuppa. Yes, I see that. But we don't need the Ritz, Paddy. We don't need the gentleman's club either.

Shall we knock it on the head, this green-finger stuff? Shall we? No I'm not trying to undermine you. You are the best site manager I ever worked with. Let's get that straight. I'm pleased with the managing. I'm pleased with the tea. I'm delighted with the security of the goods and such. It's just the flowers and the veg. You see?

Not For Me

Paddy, you know Cynthia, she said she has another year before her finals, right? Me too. You know what, people ask me what I'm going to do then, when I have the letters after my name. They think I'm going to say a lawyer or a teacher maybe. They can see me living like these folk in the Asphodels. Oh yes. My parents are the same. That's all they want for me. *Get a good job*, they say, *get a good job*. You know what they mean by that, Paddy? They mean a job with a white collar and a pension, and enough cash to live in a semi in the suburbs... in fact, to live in the Asphodels, or in one of the million places exactly like it in this green and pleasant land of ours. How can I break away, Paddy? How does a young bloke like me break away from all the dullness and take Cynthia with him... into a new life? A hippy? Oh no, I don't mean that. I mean a successful life, but as I see it, in my mind.

Yes, I *can* tell you. The semi-detached rooted life is not for me. No. See this in your head, Paddy... twenty years from now, right? There's this villa in California, with a long pool and with cacti and palm trees along a driveway. There I am, sipping coffee in my office, writing the next chapter of my new novel. Inspiration feeds into this life through the wind, the sea, the stars... I have been on the beach for two hours, then chatting about my work to a journalist in a seafront bar. In the studio at the far side of the villa there is Cynthia, working on her next portrait. She's painting some Hollywood star.

There's a massive dog stretched out on the rug... and Cynthia, she has a very special cat, maybe a

Siamese... what? Time to get the sandwiches. Okay. Yes, we'll talk again. I know you're listening. I want your advice, Paddy. You're a man of the world.

You wanted cheese and tomato, right? Fine. Chocolate biscuits. I'll get some. Milk… oh yes, you need milk. Thanks for listening, Paddy

Get Your Money On

Come on, dig deep in them pockets. A fiver each. The big race is next week, and it's ten to one now. *Dick Diver.* That's the name. You could put your mortgage on him. You know, this is the way to the life I always dreamed of. The money is going on... on the nose. Take a risk as big as a bus and before you will stretch out that golden future, lads. The golden future. I mean we're talking about a Rolls at the door of your mansion and skivvies bringing your whisky when you click your fingers... sorry to say the word *click*, Gordon me old mate. Now you can plainly see that this dream of mine, well, it'll be in Ireland. I'll be back where I was brought up, in Galway. Yes, I'll have a mansion on the cliffs and a field behind as big as Texas, full of nags, and my own brewery down the road, and I'll dress like Noel Coward, I will. So get that money out and we'll all shout for *Dick Diver*!

The truth is that in the racing game, a man has a *feeling*. That's the only way I can explain it. You look at an animal and you sort of tune in. You can see it's going to be good, to be fast, have *qualities*, lads. This one has qualities. You know, like you see in a top-level builder. *Qualities.*

I guess I learned all this from the family. Uncles and that. They were *immersed* in horses. Oh yes. Born in the saddle they were. All the skills came naturally, and they were passed on to me.

f.a.o. Dr P. Stone,

7, Asphodel Avenue,

Knotworth

Yorks

United Kingdom

Dad,

Thanks for the letter. I'm well, but things are busy, as they say. I can't sit still, as usual. It's wonderful to get into something real. People are so needy here. So grateful. There are people with horrible eye diseases and bent bones – I wish I'd studied medicine like you, then I'd know the Latin names. I never had Mum's lust for learning. Am I sounding patronising? I just wonder now why I read sociology.

  *Jill said would I become one of the Raj lot after a few weeks and there IS a struggle. Baddies – you told me about evil and Hitler. I'll never forget the day you showed me the Belsen pictures and said, '*Son, help stop the sea of evil from swallowing us and what we believe…*' Well, I'm doing my bit. How can I convey the first night? I'd need to be Shakespeare. The smell was overpowering and the light startling. Dark is different here. Its shapes are taken and reshuffled. African religion is so different – there's such joy on one side of it. I can even understand why evil has a mythology to itself.*

My new friend is called Jomo, after the famous one. He's 20, sings Bob Marley and longs for English papers to read. He speaks French and my GCSE is not up to it! But he has such a capacity for love. His voice, attitudes – everything he says and does is a sort of love for the simple things. What is real for him is just the phenomenon of food, drink, washing, praying and singing.

At school I remember my stupid history lessons and I've kept bringing them to mind here. The prat who stood in front of us, overfed with calories and imperialist crap, spent a term telling us about redcoats, Rorke's Drift and the simple black. Now the windows have been opened, and I don't just mean fresh air.

I've not asked about Mother. You say she's improving. Thank God. You're doing a great job. Thanks her for the socks and stuff. Books and magazines would be useful. Teaching means more than one blackboard and lots of talk. I'm determined to learn some of the local lingo by the way. Teaching is exhausting and now I'm going to hit the sack.

Cheers,

Phil.

She's Here Again

It's that woman, lads. Sime's not here is he... he's at number nineteen. She's coming in. Say nothing. Say nothing. Andy... get out the door now and go tell Sime to stay where he is... good lad.

Oh hello, it's Mrs Baker if I'm not mistaken. You came last week. I recall you were looking for Simon? Yes, well I'm Patrick, the number one hut officer. I look after the hut. Now if I'm not mistaken, you were saying that you were with child? Right, well, and Simon is the daddy? Oh, you're sure he is. Right. Well I have to say it seems unlikely. He's a moderate man, a great reader. Keeps himself to himself. Not the sort who spreads it about, though that sounds a bit common. I didn't mean to be common, Mrs Baker. How far are you... oh, five months! Well look if Simon has anything to do with this child, I'll be sure to tell him to contact you. Just now he's in our Leeds hut, applying some bitumen on the roof. Just leave your address on this bit of paper. There you go. Fine now. He'll be in touch. You know if he is... responsible... well, he'll make a fine father. His dad was a fine father and I'm sure the skills are passed on. Oh yes, he's reliable. You loved him? Did you? Oh don't cry now, Mrs Baker. By the way, please don't think I'm being too forward, but is there a *Mr* Baker? Oh he's flown the nest, gone for good. I understand. Absent husband. Understood. Anybody got a hanky? There's a woman here weeping. Gordon, make some tea will you, there's a good fella.

You sit yourself down here, missus. Don't worry, we have fathers here. These men are dads, most of 'em.

They know about pregnant ladies... right, Barney? Now, missus, you sit there. Men can be difficult to figure out, I know.

f.a.o. Mrs J. Hemper,

5, Roll St.,

Edinburgh

Dear Joan,

He's back! I haven't seen him about for ages, and suddenly there he was at the door. So last week he arrived with tea in a flask and some ice-buns. We sat and chatted about birds and mice, cars and hats, and anything that took our fancy, as we sipped his tea and nibbled the buns. It was glorious. I saw such a different side to the man. But that was not all. There was more, just after that.

Wait for it! He asked me out to afternoon tea! Harold next door I mean. It was so nice and he was so sweet. He took me to a posh restaurant in Leeds. It was upstairs, at the end of one of those arcades, you might recall. The waitress wore an apron and a little lacy hat – you know the kind of place. Harold was dressed in a suit, shirt and tie, even down to the waistcoat with a fob-watch in the pocket. It was like going back in time. The phrase old-fashioned gentleman comes to mind. It could have been a black and white film like we used to go to at the Rex!

So, he ordered the full complement, with cakes and sandwiches on the high cake-stand, with the tiers, you know. The sandwiches had the crusts cut off. Oh My God! I felt like a real lady. It was more like 1932 than 1972!

We didn't stop talking for hours... well, he was talking mostly, about the bomb. He seems to think the world is coming to an end and there will be nuclear bombs, poor man. We were there for two hours, before I remembered that I had to make some tea for Dr Stone, who's not well.

Romance at my age hey? Now what about you? Tell me more about that son of yours. One day he's going to be the Prime Minister by the sound of it.

But I'm still worried that he'll disappear again. That's men though, I know. They are inscrutable. He's basically very nice, but moody, I think. Poor lamb, he's missing his wife. I of course fully understand that!

Love,

Ivy

New Face

Lads, this is Al Hinchcliff. New lad. Brickie. He's working with you, Sime. Show him the ropes... ah, literally with this guy, Al, because he's a wrestler, aren't you, Sime?

Anyway Al, any problems come to me. Come to Barney. We're on a deadline, so it's all systems go, and I'm going to be bringing in some casuals as well, for the digging and that. Now this is Paddy Lanagan, he's the sort of father figure round here, right Paddy? Sime is Mr Muscle. Gordon... say hello, Gordon... he's an all-rounder I suppose.

Now, I've got another team of lads at the top end... Asphodel Crescent. They sometimes join us. Yes, but really, this little lot here... they're finishing off. Most of the hard work is done. We're aiming at middle of August I suppose. Most of all, have a good time, work hard and have a laugh when you can.

No, gardening is not part of the work you're signing up for. That's Paddy's handiwork. Thinks he's a farmer in between pouring tea and cleaning spades.

The Maori Maleroa

'Ladies and gentleman, in the blue corner we have the Masked Avenger... fierce and evil. And in the red corner, the gruesome painted face of the wild man from the southern hemisphere, The Maori Maleroa.' That's what he'll say and I'll come out like, you see, Andy. Now don't tell the others. But well, you're a student, a clever lad. You have a brain. I can trust you not to say a word to that lot of philistines in that hut. See, he's the real me, the Maori... the world sees this builder, a brickie, carrying this hod, leaping about the roof, a man covered in mortar and sweat. Well, inside here... there's The Maori Maleroa! You won't say a word will you, Andy. It's a secret. But I had to tell somebody, and you're a man to be trusted. See, you can't have a career as a wrestler with a name like Simon Slack. You follow?

I'm going to have that big break soon. I can feel it coming on. The next fight is with Larry Lumberjack. Big man. Solid as an oak. When he hits the canvas he shakes the walls of the market hall. Now if I can beat him next week, I'll be noticed. You see? Noticed. I mean on telly and that.

Andy, people just do not know what dedication is needed to be a pro in the wrestling game. Oh no. I mean, for one thing, you have to learn to throw yourself around like a doll. You have to know how to react to a punch when in fact there is no punch. It's just a slap of the flesh, you see. Course I have a *haka* and that. To all intents and purposes I'm a Maori. Most folk believe it... though there is this woman who always sits on the front row at Forley

130

Town Hall and she screams abuse at me. *'You're Simon Slack from Spratley and I knew your mother! She was a whore!'* That's what she says. One time, when my head was being trodden on, and there I was, staring at her screaming, red-raw face, she moves up close to the ropes and she looks me in the eye and she says, *'Your mother was a whore, and you're not a Maori!'* She shouted it like some wild moron. I had to laugh, even though The Batley Bonecrusher had me in his best hold.

To: Mr P. Stone,

Centre 223, Fair Lawns,

Nairobi,

Kenya

Dear Phil,

Your postmark wasn't Nairobi. Where are you? With the Bushmen? Your letter told me nothing. You were just the same at prep. Mother sends kisses. She's in a lot of pain now and still can't write a word. But she's sitting by the window, managing to smile. We had a glorious autumn walk today. It's Friday and the kids were still at school. The park was quiet and I pushed mum up to the fields where they play football on a Sunday afternoon. There's a pond beyond that with ducks and an old bandstand. It brought to mind when we used to escape out of her parents' way for a while, when we were courting.

Today it was about two o'clock when we settled down with the coffee and chatted about birds and the passersby. We played that game of guessing what they were. Mum thought they were mostly retired, except for one chap in miserable denims, hands in pockets and underfed, all muscle and scrubbed flesh. Mum said we should offer him a sandwich but nowadays you see a stranger and a nervy voice inside says, 'Mugger, thief, robber...' We all have that voice so there's a strained, unwilling silence between us. Or is this all simply in my liberal, over-educated mind, a product of the Forties when we used to talk about everything all day – between lectures and bombings?

It's later now and I've returned to the letter, alone while Mother sleeps. I'm in the study – your old room. Let me bring England the beautiful, ageing, gorgeous old girl, into your head. The evening is breezy and the last light is just holding on, living on borrowed time. The lamp by the bus stop outside sheds a sort of ochre haze over the hedges and the dogwood and holly seem to be amber in their stringy branches. The garden birds are playing pop with each other, fighting over a fatball. The forsythia is dull now but the bare cherry is still lovely, even out of Housman's season.

Best of all – don't call me a peeping tom – is a pair of young lovers at the bus stop. I can hear every word. They're 17 or so. I'm naughty, listening, but it's fascinating. He seems to be one of these scruffy Rocker types, ginger-haired and puny. She is petite, slight. A very angel, frail and dressed to perfection. So rare these days. This is the third night they've waited noisily for the number 52 bus. They chat for half an hour about new records and about hair. He is as interested in hairstyles as she! Not short back and sides like you!

Reality will set in, as it does. She'll be along to see me about one of the usual problems. She'll sit there and mope. It's best to give them all they need. But I see hope in them sometimes, like this moment.

Your mother is knitting you a sweater. She read something about Africa having terribly cold nights. Is this true? It wouldn't hurt to write a proper letter, old man. Must go – Mr. Navin's come ready for the play – a local amateur thing – Othello I think. I seem to recall that it does get chilly out there. Look after yourself, son. It's a wild old world beyond the white cliffs of Dover!

Take care.

Dad

Advice to the Young

You, young fella, what's your name... Andy? Right Andy, mine's a pint of bitter. You're a good lad, I can see that. That's young Cynthia at the bar. She's beautiful as any woman on the cover of a magazine and I've told her so.

Now sit there. I'll have to put my leg on that stool... damned arthritis. I was shot in that very knee at a scrap in Burma. Six of them jumped me as I walked back from the thunderbox in the Kana Wong clearing, you'll find it on the map, six miles from Pusan. Oh yes, I was a P.O.W. That's what I want to say to you, son. Get out now while you still have legs and a todger! Yes, don't get stuck in Asphodel bloody Way. You are looking at Schofield Murgatroyd, soldier of fortune! Oh yes, that's on my passport... soldier of fortune. The officials always stare at me when they read that. But I stare 'em out, lad... stare 'em out. Be afraid of nothing in this world, son, nothing.

There I was, in darkest Kana Wong, and this man, face like a rat and stinking like a midden, he confronts me and jabs out a blade the length of Filey Bay... bloody bastard he was. I swiped him with my cricket bat and he squealed for mercy! Now, anyway, I wanted to say, ask her out! I've seen you looking at her... Cynthia of course. Faint heart never won fair lady, and by Lord Montgomery, my old pal, she is a catch! Grab her now or some brainless buffoon will have her first! Go on.

The Murgatroyds, son, they always took what they wanted... grab it first and ask questions later. My great grandfather was at Waterloo. Oh yes, first man into the

135

attack with the West Shropshires... caught one in the groin. Fortunately the cricket balls were still spinning if you follow me. Damned good pint this. Another would not go amiss... thank you, son. Thank you. Now when you go to the bar, tell that young lady that her eyes are gorgeous and you long to kiss them... and that she has a face like Helen of troy. These cultured bints, they love that classical talk.

Did you ask her? No? Oh, son, son, where's the mettle in you? Where's the spunk in the blood? Take hold of her, son, take hold! Faint heart and all that. And by God, she is a fair lady!

Andrew, listen... how did we win the war? By being scared but never showing it. You walked towards the bullets. You knew there were snipers out there. But you walked on. Same with love. It's a very unnerving prospect, but the rewards for the brave are greater than pots of gold. Walk out there, son, tell her. Then kiss her. Women like a man who takes the lead you see. That's why they fall for military men. When I was in uniform, they *swarmed* around me. No, I know you can't wear a uniform... though you could join the Salvation Army. I've known chaps who've done that just to attract the fair sex. Straight up, I have.

Take the lead, *tell* her she's having a meal with you. Don't ask her if she's free. Faint heart never won fair whatsit...

Mrs. I Carver,

3, Asphodel Avenue,

Knotworth,

Yorks.

Dear Ivy,

I thought it was all settled after your report about having tea with Harold! Now he's gone back into his shell again. What's his problem? Is it something to do with his worries about the bomb?

What a shame he didn't turn up! What with you making the patio all lovely and covered in flowers for the occasion. Are you sure he wasn't poorly? Of course you do know he's most likely on some strong medication? Yes, I've known widowers before. They hold it all in. They know they have to be strong, and so they put on a front for the world. Yes, I've known plenty of men like that. He was probably in a sulk, or in tears, and couldn't face you - couldn't face the situation I mean.

Give him another chance, Ivy. He seems fine to me. He seems like a good man. But more important, how are you? Write me a real letter and give me a good idea of how you are. Tell me if I'm wrong but you never mention your friends. I remember you had a lot of friends. You were in that historical society I think, and that group that did watercolours. I wouldn't like to think that you had gone into a shell and hidden from the world and your old friends.

Anyway, I was thinking the other day about that time we went to Bempton Cliffs and I nearly knocked you off into the North Sea. Do you remember that you said, 'Don't worry, I'd have landed on that ledge, with the sea birds'?

I think he's very shy, this neighbour of yours. Try being a bit more pushy. The best way to beat loneliness is to burst out of it, like a chick from its shell. Someone told me that once – or was it in Woman's Weekly?

Take your pleasures where you can, Sis. We're a long time dead - as far as we know!

Love

Joan

This Hut

Jim, I'm writing home from Old England, missing home like hell. I'm feeling so homesick I just wanted to write home and give you the annual report on your big brother Patrick. I'm still on the site at Knotworth in Yorkshire, and my special responsibility is with the hut - quite a project.

Thanks so much for the wise words regarding Renee. I will give it a shot. I have a decent set of clothes, but of course, I'm short of the spondulix because I have it all invested. But what I'll do is give her a treat in my hut - the full gentlemanly treatment. We'll have a banquet. I just hope she knows my failings. But you said some wise words when you pointed out that it's a clean slate and I can start again. Yes, she must like me, in spite of the moods I had when we gave it a go last time. There we are then, off we go with the courting again. Lord help me!

Have *you* ever thought about a hut, Jim? It's a very special thing. You know, it's a home for a bunch of hairy-arsed labourers on the loose, homeless sons of the soil, lost sons and husbands making an honest cent. Oh yes, my responsibility is to make it like a little welcoming home for them.

It's fifteen feet by twelve but I've made a lean-to for the lavvy. There's a thick doormat so they can stamp their feet when they come in, and the kettle is on all day. We have plates, mugs and serviettes – and a big pan for soup. I've put a print of Dublin on one wall – it shows the Four Courts. Then I took a beermat from the local Club and nailed that to another wall. It says *Fazackerly's Ales* on it... in green and black. Then of course there's the calendar so I can mark off the working days and the bad weather days. Oh, and a first-aid box. I don't like bragging, but I'm a dab-hand with plasters and liniments. Accidents are few and far between but Gordon did twist his ankle last week, and before that he cut his thumb open.

So you see it's a little home from home. Think of me next Sunday, because I'm going to play on the whistle for the lads, a sort of little concert. *The Curragh of Kildare* will ring out across the Asphodels, followed by *The Fields of Athenry* and they'll not be a dry eye in the hut at all. I'm buying in paper hankies.

How are you doing at the new posting, by the way? Arrested any villains yet? I always knew that the Garda was the job for you. You always had a bullying streak in you, and you were a bugger for uniforms. God help the thieves and drunkards around Galway today.

Streamline is still doing well, I hear. Not long now. I have thirty pounds on him. The trainer tells me that the aim is for the big races at York. I have thirty on him for next Saturday anyway, and he's a long shot. I got twenty to one. Get some on, make a few quid, why don't you?

Your loving brother,

Patrick

Hooky and the Holy Book

Look, it's here, clear as day. The world is going to come to a sticky end. It's in the great book, the Bible itself. I bet you never read the Bible, Simon. I know you have, Paddy. You're a man of belief. The Irish know all about the Good Lord and they fear Him, as they bloody well should. I tell you one thing. He's after me. Oh yes he is. He's stalking me. I did wrong. I wronged them women. I was a bad husband. I see the truth now. I was selfish. I hadn't learned what love was. Now I see it as it really is.

So you think I'm talking tripe do you, Simon? Well look to yourself before you cast the ruddy stone, mate. Just tell me this. What do you see when you look at me? You see an ordinary bloke, red hair, five-feet ten, spots on his face, flushed, a beer belly. You see a man crushed under life's pressures. But no, that is not the real thing. The real thing is inside, and it's something none of you can see. It's a hardness. I've been hard inside and I've not let love come through. I was hard to those poor women. I see that now. Never again will I chat up a woman. No. If there's to be wife number four, then she'll be treated like a princess, she will.

It's all there in print. You must let love breathe. A man has to see with more than his eyes. He must see with his heart.

Yes, Paddy. I know there's a wall to plaster at number eight. I'll be there *toute suite*. That's French. I'm learning ten French words every day. I'm after a French woman. A French wife is the only one a man needs. Truly feminine they are. Truly strong but genuinely women. Like of Bardot! Yes, I'm going, Paddy, I'm going.

The Other Al Hinchcliff

The bag, Paddy? Oh it's my change of clothes. Oh yes, when I finish here I'm off into Capsworth – stand-up. I do stand-up. Don't be so surprised. You might have heard of me. I'm not Al Hinchcliff when I'm on that stage. No. I'm Uncle Albert. Well, what's he then? I'll tell you. He's the Yorkshireman from the stories, the old tales. He's everybody's character uncle. The man who drinks too much, has a flutter, annoys everybody, tells tall tales. Flat cap, beer, catching rabbits and living on scraps. That's Uncle Albert. In the bag I've got cap, check shirt, waistcoat, old pants with holes in 'em... all that.

Oh yes I make some pocket money out of him. I'll get thirty quid for tonight. That's not to be sniffed at, is it, Paddy? Course, in this game you wait to be discovered, signed up. No, I mean signed up for television or radio... my hero is Al Read. You don't know Al Read? *Eh, if he cuts your ear off can I have it?* That's his voice. I did his voice. He's a radio star. You must have heard him!

You'll have to come and hear me... I'll tell the lads.

At the Bar

They'll be here any minute, Lisa. The horrible rain has shut down the work again. Please let it soon be September and college! Please let it come soon. Though there is one consolation - Andy. He is so shy, but well, you have to fancy him. He looks like Steve McQueen. He has that very short crew-cut and he looks very athletic. I think he writes poetry. One of the older men dropped a hint about that. Still, every time I feel bored out of my skull in here I think of how much I'll have saved when term starts. It's worth it all for that. Have to go now. Ring again soon, Lisa.

Rain, rain, rain. Oh here they are. That loud one going on about his horses and the big race... the one who only talks about his illness... oh and there's the student. The others told me he was a student. He's very shy. Maybe I should make the first move and ask him about himself. *'Pint of bitter? Yes of course.'*

What I'll do is count the flowers on the wallpaper. It says in the magazine I've been reading that when you have to do a boring job, you play games in your head. *'Oh a bottle of brown ale, coming up!'*

Oh, here he comes. It's the student. *'Half a pint of bitter? Course. I'm Cynthia by the way. Oh, you knew that?'* He's been asking about me. I knew he fancied me, I just knew.

'You been busy then?' I asked him. He sort of blushed. One day he'll speak. The shy ones usually have a lot of words saved up, waiting to be released, like prisoners.

Mr T. Stone,

Centre 223, Fair Lawns,

Nairobi,

Kenya

Dear Tom,

We got your letter and the stuff you wanted is on its way. You've given Mother nightmares about ants of course. That's Celia all over. I'm in your room again and all is peaceful for a while. Generally it's noisy, our England. Dirty, too. I go outside in the morning, wind and traffic have blown the litter in heaps by the gate and there are piles of cigarettes, crisps and garbage knee-deep. Worst of all are the beer cans.

I'm becoming obsessive about noise and dirt as I grow older. But I don't want to whine about the pristine days of youth. The point is, why do we foully despise ourselves and our own? What about you? I'm interested in your work, Phil. You must tell me more about how you teach. You have clearly been deeply affected by Africa and it can't be only the weather.

The crab apple is shedding tons of fruit and leaves and I keep sweeping them etc. To an outsider it must seem as though the garden is too much for an old buffer, but I adore the simplest tasks. I take a profound pleasure in making compost and using it at the right time on the corner patch.

*Do you have time to listen to music? I know how much you love it. **I'm listening to Brahms now – the Academic Festival overture you like.** I've had a Mahler spell and become morbidly introspective, even started writing a bit. The poetry you know. But Brahms is a bit heavy as well. Someone said he was like an old tetchy bear. I know the feeling.*

By the way, my couple are there. Almost every night. The boy is serious now: I can hear them clearly. Your mother thinks it's odd but I feel somehow responsible for them. They've taken shelter in my eaves and I house them. I've heard them confess things that I'm sure their own parents will never have heard. Does that sound idiotic? It's as if they know I'm there. Phil, you're becoming a sort of diary for me. We only ever talked football and model planes, didn't we? Your 18 years with us has been only a bed and breakfast affair. I feel I let you down.

But these two kids – it sounds silly but I think they're dreaming for me. Perhaps someone overheard me saying similar things and some branches of elm in the street in deepest Tykeland still trap my first real words. Anyway, it would be nice if you were here for Saturday's game. When are you due home? You could ring, if you like. It would be great to hear your voice. Your mother would love that.

Dad

The Legs Question

No, seriously, Sime, is the right leg longer than the left? I noticed it this morning when I caught a glimpse of myself in that mirror Paddy put up in the corner. The right leg is distinctly longer – an inch I'd say. What do you think? I know what you're thinking. You're thinking it's Gordon again, worrying over nothing. But it matters. I mean, it explains why I was never good at sports at school. I always had a wonky run. The games master said so. He said he wasn't going to enter me for any sprints because I was *ungainly*. Now, that's a funny word. What does ungainly suggest to you, Sime? Be honest. Clumsy? Is that what you think it means? Well there you go then, I was always a clutz. They never gave me a chance to shine. I sat in the changing rooms reading *The Beano* when the others were all out sprinting and leaping.

So is it a bit longer? You think so? It might be the way I'm standing. I'm going to ask Sime, as he's a wrestler. He's fit as a flea. Watch me walk over the floor, then see if it shows. Right?

There. Is the right a bit longer than the left? You think so? Can they put that right? Do they... do they stretch it? What? You wear special shoes. Oh God, no. I already wear a corset and a truss. Thanks for trying to help anyway. You're a real pal.

My theory is that, when I was young, I used to hump bags of concrete around, and the weight shifted, unnaturally like, to one side. So that one leg did a lot of work and the other one rested. So, over the years, one leg was stretched.

I'll be off to see the quack about it, just wait and see. Dr Smedley will sort it out, soon as he looks at me.

The Faulty Lock

I'm sorry, Al. It's me, Andy. I'm stuck in this loo. The lock is crap. Can you come up and force the door? Cheers. Five minutes, okay. Ye gods, how embarrassing! I'm stuck in a brand-new toilet on Asphodel Way. This is supposed to be the street of the future, streamlined, paradise Britain. Fine. Here I am stuck in the loo. Worst thing is, I'm supposed to be meeting Cynthia... well, ten minutes ago. Come on, Al, shake a leg.

Look at this door... it's thin as a matchbox. What do they make these places out of- balsa wood?

Oh you're there. Can you move the knob, Al? Just turn it as you hold the thin part with a spanner. You haven't got a spanner? Can you get one?

He's gone to fetch one from the hut. She'll never talk to me again. I'll be so late! Women like men to be on time. They like organised blokes, not dreamers like me. Oh Christ, why am I doing this job? Cash, of course. I'm thinking of what I'll spend the cash on back at college.

Oh, Al. A spanner... good, try again. No? One more time. Jesus! Al, kick it in. Just kick it in! Why can't you do that? Kick it in... I'll mend it. What? Go and fetch Barney then. Oh shite! That's my one and only chance with the woman I love... gone!

Dear Barney,

I am writing on a rather odd topic, but it is something that has caused some irritation here at the company. It may seem like a very minor matter, but it is indicative of a wastage of resources and possibly a complete failure to grasp the nature of a site materials store. I have been reliably informed by one of my travelling supervisors that the hut and the compound at the heart of your base for work at the Asphodels, managed by Mr Patrick Lanagan, has been unnecessarily adorned.

When I say 'adorned' I refer to the hut, or shed, used by Mr Lanagan, which appears to have been given a coat of light blue paint, and also has a flower garden along one side. These measures are surely completely irrelevant to the workings of such an installation.

I would appreciate a toning-down of such furnishing and decoration. Could you have a strong word with Mr Lanagan, please, Barney, and remind him that such a hut or shed is a purely functional and utilitarian building - a place where workers may come for tools and materials, and of course, for a refreshing cup of tea during their official breaks?

I do appreciate the need to make the working atmosphere social and friendly, but growing enough vegetables to feed a platoon of sappers is a little over the top, I feel.

I feel sure that you, an experienced foreman, appreciate the importance of an economical use of space. Of course, we appreciate that there have been no thefts

150

from the site, and that may be because of Mr Lanagan's presence there. In which case, we do feel a slight sense of obligation to the man.

Yours sincerely,

Nigel Bentham-Caldwell

Sandwich Time

I'm out of corned beef, Andy. Sorry. But everything else is as ordered. Paddy wanted extra chips and I've done some for him... here. Now, I was telling you about that time I was a home help... well the truth is, we were all sort of nurses really, as well as being skivvies. Oh yes, terrible work, but such a valuable thing to do. I mean, these poor old men, these men who have served their country... fought the Nazis or the Japanese... well, now here they are, bed-ridden or something. Me and my mates, we used to get on the bike and do a rota... make them breakfast, clean their bedclothes, wipe them clean... all that.

I miss it though – all that helping the poor old folk, caring for the sick. It was all going well, for years, and then the mistake. Anyone can slip at some point. Just a tiny little mistake with some medicine and... well, disaster. Here I am, serving at a corner shop. It was a mistake made by too much caring, I have to say. All I did was give a man a painkiller without asking the doc.

Rain again! This blasted country hey? We should have moved to the sun long ago. I kept nagging my Albert to move us to somewhere warm but he was lazy, bless him. I always dreamed of living on an island in the Med. Malta... I love Malta. We went there once, but you know what, Andy.... in Malta they eat little songbirds! They do. They trap the little darlings in cages on the hills and then they eat them! Barbaric, that's what it is.

Enjoy the sandwiches. Fine day tomorrow I think!

Mr T. Stone,

Centre 223, Fair Lawns,

Nairobi,

Kenya

Dear Tom,

Thank God you sent the card. Good to know that all is well. Mum is gardening! She seems better today. People still come to me with their health problems – friends, I mean. Every headache becomes a migraine, but I think the only illness I ever had was sheer dreaminess! I'm staring out of the window, wondering whether glass splinters on the wall might deter thieves and vandals. Mrs Tern was burgled last week. My fence has been kicked in again. Maybe that little moron came back in vengeance? I'm sure I saw him, just two nights back, staring in from the memorial mason's place about 30 yards up from us on that side – you recall?

We were here before the Asphodels were developed. I feel as though I'm clinging on to a scrap of old rural England, while all the modern stuff starts throttling us. I guess the locals see me as the curmudgeon.

My lovers seem to have stopped coming. Talk of marriage does it – alters things like a rainstorm in July. It's so silent here anyway. I've made a den of your room – a proper study. Bookshelves, cassette player, a board for postcards. That photo of you playing cricket at seven – that's there. One of Mother trying crazy golf. There's my Welsh dragon, too. I've been an honorary Welshman since leaving my college. I suppose Yorkshire and my own people had something missing and emotional Wales filled the vacuum.

Africa will do that for you. I'm fighting off sleep as I write. Hope you enjoyed the glider book. I can see you at eight, running down the slopes in the Marches – Shrewsbury it was – and your dad puffing behind. The trees staggered around us in time, and they and the lovers' words all around in the gusts, like my two young hearts here.

The trees are so lovely in England. Are they in Kenya? They would have to be splendid to beat the trees I see every morning.

Write soon.

Dad.

Passion's Slaves

Yes, I really am a wrestler. Honest, I am, yes. No, I don't fight with my real name. I have a stage-name. I'm the Maori Maleroa. I do a *haka*. Ah no, don't tickle me there... no, no, oh I can't stand being tickled, Mrs Dinchop. Yes, I *will* call you Denise.

Oh Mrs Dinchop... Mrs Dinchop... Denise... you are beautiful. I've been full of desire for you since you first waved a duster across your front door! I love those breasts, little soft hills... I could kiss 'em all day. Oh Denise, I'm guessing your other half doesn't provide all this, eh love? I know, I know, a woman needs some loving. I know that, darlin.' Now I'm going to screw you till you scream for mercy... thank God for the bloody rain. No bugger knows where I am, darlin.' Nobody at all.

He's a traveller, you say, Mr Dinchop? Lingerie? Gone for a week maybe. Oh well, I can entertain you then... I love your giggle, Denise.

I could love you all day and night, Denise. Mr Dinchop is a fool. We work up a terrific rhythm you and me. I love that slap and sweat you get with a proper woman. You're a real full-blooded woman, Denise! By God you are.

I hope this house has got thick walls! Oh, you're right. I built it so I should know! Daft isn't it? It's that groan you do, like it's real passion... do I do that to you, Denise? Oh my God let's go again!

155

Chairs

Now Patrick, I see you've been making some garden chairs. Very nice. Very sort of countryman... these are for the outside then? Right. I can see that they're for reclining, as when a gardener would rest from his labours and such. So you're sawing down the legs so that they are like armchairs to lie back on... very clever. You're a dab-hand with wood, Patrick.

The only thing is, as I've said before, and I'm trying very hard not to explode now, Patrick, the day will come when Mr Bentham-Caldwell and his minions will descend. Do you recognise the name, my friend? Yes, he is the man who comes to check all the work, as the deadline is reached... yes, inspection time. You have met him before. Now Mr Bentham-Caldwell and three men in grey suits arrive in a black car resembling a hearse, and they hold clipboards, and what do they do? Yes, they check the quality of our workmanship. BUT THEY DON'T CHECK BLOODY ARMCHAIRS FOR THE HUT... sorry, sorry, I didn't mean to snap. It's been a hard day... and it's starting to rain again... I'm going to sit down...

But I'm sorry. I have to be calmer. I'm on the tablets now. This job is more stressful than the army, let me tell you. There's deadlines. I hate the word- *deadline.* It sounds like a death-knell, don't you think? *You have a deadline... one week to the deadline...* it's like torture, Patrick, old mate. I'd rather be a Tommy and go over the top. At least you know where you are with a sniper. They aim at your bonce. But when some faceless git reminds you about a deadline, they do it like a midnight attack with a stiletto, like a sort of whisper. Then you can't sleep for thinking of the word.

It's still a July deadline, just. Though I'm thinking August now. Mr Bentham-Caldwell will not like that.

Yes, I'll need an armchair... see you later, Patrick.

Albert in Action

Evening you lot! It's me again - your favourite comic. I'm going to tell you about my Uncle Albert - a real old-world Yorkshireman. They don't breed 'em like him any more... what's that? Thank God! You can mock, but he was always there when needed was Albert... he fought in both world wars.

Na then. How can I start to describe my Uncle Albert? Well, we'll start with him as the Poet Laureate of Complainers. Like some husbands take up marquetry or making plastic kits, he took up chelp. He had a room for it at home, custom-built. His moaning were usually related to his illnesses. When his piles were throbbing the front room were turned into Auschwitz. My Aunty Bessy used to pretend to hoover the shed just to keep out of his way. Complaining were a vocation to him. He practised in front of a mirror – screwing up his nose, frowning and saying, 'Typical bloody government' in different voices. He said it one way for the bus queue, one way for the bookies, and a specially irritating way for the saloon bar.

T' barber shop were his real arena. The language coming from under that cloth were bad enough to offend Bernard Manning. Many a time he nearly had a lug lopped off. T' barber had patience o' Job. Failure were the hallmark of his life. If he'd lived in Siberia, he'd have tried grave-digging as a career. He once tried selling cheap team shirts outside Barnsley's ground. Only they were green. He was the sort o' bloke folk looked at and somehow knew that he'd never make owt. At school, he made a poker. It took him a whole term. It were bent and

158

evil. His mother said, 'Don't leave that in City Square. Some criminal is sure to do murder with it.'

Course, his speciality were food. He deeply resented any food put in front of him that weren't flesh. My Aunty Bessy tried to pass off a nut cutlet as a bit o' tongue once. Within half a minute she were in the shed again. He had problems with eating: he only had half a stomach but he could fart like an elephant. It were a mystery. This had another side effect. He used to get a bad attack of the scutters if he ate too much rich food. He had to work hard to hold it in. He developed a walk with bum cheeks closed, clamped tight like. When he passed certain parts o' Leeds he got cat-calls.

I should also mention Albert's religious persuasion. He was the only member of the Plymouth Brethren to live in Batley. Course, the place has a bad reputation. Folk in Huddersfield say Batley folk eat their first-born, I'm told. But he saw God as a sort of headmaster and that folk had to try to be prefects and win house points. The problem was, the Devil kept hitting you and he had a gang. God's gang were always somewhere else when you needed them, he said, supping tea and eating muffins by a log fire.

Course, he had a birthmark like – well, a posterior - on his belly. But Bessy never saw it. Never saw his naked flesh except to put his corn-pads on. Even that didn't count. It were more like geology than treating skin.

Albert got a questionnaire through the post once, him being a farming bloke. It were from some academic

*type at Leeds University and it were about diseases o'
sheep like. In the space provided, Albert put down, 'has
heft. Very bad.' When this stumped the professors, they
wrote back for an explanation.*

'Heft,' *he said.* 'Has Every F-------- Thing.'

*He had bad eyesight. Folk thought he'd been down
t' pit in the war – a reserved occupation like. Truth is,
he'd ruined his eyes studying form wearing his mother's
glasses. The racehorses were his obsession. He said he
had systems. Like, maybe a hoss would wink at him in the
paddock. Or sometimes he'd back the one that evacuated
itself before the race.* 'That'll beat the handicapper!' *he
used to shout.*

*I don't know why it was, but wherever and
whenever he was involved in some sort of public event, it
caused embarrassment. Like at his sister Frances'
funeral. His brother Ossie at the speech said,* 'To Albert,
Fanny were the most important thing in his life.'

*Thank you ladies and gentlemen... I'm Al
Hinchcliff and you've heard all about my Uncle Albert...*

Dr P. Stone,

7, Asphodel Avenue,

Knotworth,

United Kingdom

Dear Both,

A real letter! My teaching fills the hours and in my spare time I talk and talk. There are five of us here with no television so we talk and talk about life, lessons and home. One is from Sheffield and the others are Londoners. I never knew people could talk so much. We sometimes get really deep – like I never did at uni!

Thanks for the home comforts – sweets and books came. Trust you to send historical novels (hysterical novels you called them, Mum!). I like the Elizabethan James Bond one. I also have a pair of lovers! They are only twelve or so, but dote on each other. The drills turn into a sing-song and they dance and smile the words, even with inane stuff like, 'How much are the apples?'. *Their faces light up.*

Yes - Africa is to me what Wales was to you, Dad. The beauty rubs off. Being in teaching here makes you speak like some word-mechanic you know. 'How's your past perfect going mate? Like me to take a look?'

'Cheers – been sounding a bit cranky lately.'

My tool kit is a grammar book, cassette library and English passport, proving that I've been exposed to the BBC and blessed with a condescending attitude to the rest of the world. I'm becoming a cynical ex-pat.

I might be home in spring. Not for Christmas. Could you send some cake? And any bits and pieces for use in lessons – anything typically British? And Dad, don't play the Lord of the Manor. Buy a dog. Get the cops. There's trouble here too, 50 miles away it seems. All down to poverty and deprivation. Rich and poor are separate as two ends of a rift valley. You find sewers and stink at one end of town and mansions at the other.

If I'm not home then, it's because I've got some kind of money opportunity – I mean some private tuition. I think the English language is the best asset I have. It's always in demand somewhere.

Love,

Tom.

True Love Running Rough

Is that Cynthia? Cynthia, it's Andy. Don't put the phone down... no, it wasn't my fault. I was... I was wanted at the site. An emergency. Yes, honest. A wall fell down. Nearly crushed Paddy. We all had to join in and put it right. You see, this wall, if any more of it had fallen it could have hurt children, or old folks. It was teetering... it was maybe ten feet high. Oh, more damage could have been done. Yes, even me! So sorry. I was so looking forward to... what? How do you mean, lying? I'm not lying. Locked in... who told you? Oh, Al Hinchcliff. I see. Well, maybe just a little fib... no, I don't make a habit of lying... wait, Cynthia... don't go, don't go! What do you mean, I'm teetering! Don't go!

Cynthia... listen. No, it was not a bad lie. It was a lie that would stop you from thinking the worst of me... you must see that. What bloke would like his girlfriend to think he was shut in a bog... I mean, a toilet? Come on, I had to spin a yarn. Cynthia... you still there?

Clock-Watching

Is that you, Dot? I'm just ringing home to say I'll be late. I'll have to do some jobs when the rain holds off, as it's supposed to do, later. But this shower I've got with me... I thought I knew them, love, I really did.

I don't know. I just don't know. There is no way a man can figure out this damned crew I'm stuck with. It's like there's a lethargy on them all. Idle ruddy slackers they are, apart from the lad. He keeps asking for jobs. Then they look at him as if he's a turncoat, against the ruddy union. There's this unwritten law in the building trade: any sign of untoward weather and it's into the hut. The damned hut – I feel like burning it down. It's wood, it's long, it's too solid and warm. It welcomes the layabouts. I mean, it stinks of sausages and bacon.

What would the sods do if, one day, they turn up and cast their eyes on a smoking heap of burnt wood where their hut was? What would they bloody do then?

It rains, then they brew up. Then the lad is sent for sweets. Then they brew up again. The Irishman starts his stories - the damned horse stories. Then it's afternoon and they have food, and then it rains again. More stories. Then it's four o'clock and off they go to the Working Men's Club. That's a bloody laugh - it's the Idle Buggers' Club if you ask me. Then the worst thing is, I have to be the good, understanding boss and join 'em.... join 'em... and with a *smile*! I ask you! *A smile.*

They sit there and they watch the clock. Maybe they play draughts. Or maybe darts. Then they brew up.

Then one looks at the clock. *'Half past two,'* he says. *'Soon be time for the Club.'* Clock-watching. Should be a job in that. *'What did you do today, Paddy? I watched a clock.'* Then there's the rain. I'm sure the sods do a rain-dance like in the westerns. Oh yes, they just want to slope off to the Club down the road, moan about the rain and play darts, or listen to that old bore who won the war all by himself. I can't stand it there. I have to sit in a corner and pray for the sun to break through. Damn the British weather – it's the construction industry's blight.

Maybe we should move to Spain, Dot. What do you think?

The worst thing is, they're so ignorant of the big world out there, sitting in this damned hut. Only yesterday in Derry there was a damned battle! The protestants were having a demonstration... peaceful... supposed to be... then a battle. There's no other word for it. But this lot... they talk horses or football pools or some rubbish.

I despair of them. I do. I despair. See you tonight, love.

Mr T. Stone,

Centre 223, Fair Lawns,

Nairobi,

Kenya

Dear Tom,

You know when you virtually FEEL a presence and turn around? There was this face at the side window. It was awful. He fixed a look at me – white and still he was, but then gone in a second. I was stupid and took a poker to the door and walked to the lawn. I shouted for the bastard to show himself but it was all still. I'd had too much cheap wine. Certainly, I'll put that glass on the wall. The gate's the weak spot. But listen to me – it's only a storm in a teacup. Thank goodness your mother was asleep. The new drugs knock her out.

Or was I imagining it? I have reasons to doubt myself:

First, I dream a lot. Do dreams work into reality?

Second, I hear things when there's nothing there

Finally, I've started talking to myself.

It's good to hear news about your colleagues and it seems you've stumbled across something radical. Found some direction? I've only ever drifted in life. A steady GP but I've had my bees. You know what Virgil said about them? 'They form a line, and drive out the idle bands of drones from the hives.' *I reckon I've done some driving out on our street!*

Mother's been a touch worse. Observable degeneration (doctor's hat on). She still manages to do a few things though. She still smiles, bless her. She was always tougher than I was. And the team are going down as well. To cap it all, my lovers have disappeared again. I make a point of sitting in the study listening. I may even invite them in for a hot toddy if they return.

What a shame about Christmas. It would have cheered Mother up. Can't you fix it? A family feast would be absolute bliss! The fire, and the tree and you with your guitar eh? Kenya sounds a bit nightmarish. Don't go near any of those slum places. I was looking in the atlas and I believe you're in Nakuru – not far from Nairobi, is it? It can be gun law down there, I'm told.

I'd best be off. If you want to be left with a topic – evil! Is it absence of good? I recently read an article by a theologian going on about when you say there's good, you say that evil exists to maintain that good. It passes the long warm summer nights. My motto is: 'To be happy is to be perpetually employed'. Must start washing. The whites are in a bundle. Impressed?

Now, remember my advice: go very steadily and carefully where you are now. There are so many dangers. But I think of you all the time.

Dad.

Not Another Thing

You'll never guess what happened this morning? I was getting dressed – just pulling my trousers up my legs, balancing as you do on one leg, and I went dizzy! Oh God it was terrible! I went back, rolled across the corner of the bed, and then my body sort of lurched down, and as I went towards the floor, there was the open drawer, left open after I took my socks out of it, and *crack!* my head slammed against the drawer corner. I've a bruise the size of a plum here... see? Why oh why does it always happen to me?

I was given a duff body, at birth, from the very start. Yes, God dished out a third-rate body. *'Oh it's only Gordon, give him the reject body on the back shelf.'* God said that, and I was doomed.

I know, it's fate. A strange fate. Some bugger up there... and I'm not blaming the Almighty Father himself, as I believe he's good like... but somebody up there has it in for me... for me, personally. I mean there I was, doing an ordinary thing, the same thing that you lot were all doing, and *wham!* I could be dead now, instead of standing here talking to my mates!

As I stand here now, it's a miracle I'm here to lay bricks at all. You're looking at a man with arthritis in one knee; an imbalance in the legs, so that he limps; impetigo in its early stages; two dislocated fingers; an ingrowing toenail; spasms in the upper arm, and only one lung fully functioning...

What Paddy? The quack? Well I would get some rogering done if I had a woman, but... come out with you? You're joking. Type of woman you pick up, they're fallen women... fallen women... I know you think I should catch a few... no thank you. I'll stay in and make my bookshelves.

Mind you, the click has gone. I tested it this morning, before I fell over. I turned rapidly, to the side and back, again and again, and... no click! It's a step forward. Mind you, they will laugh, oh yes they will. Cruel isn't the word. That lot, sitting around that old table, they would take the piss out of a man for being blind, they would. Cruel, heartless they are. But wait until one day Old Nick strikes at them and *wham!* They will know the hell of a weak body, a body open to all the little niggles and stabs of pain that Mother Nature chucks at us. Just let them wait and see, the buggers.

I think the click was brought on by the beetroot I had last weekend. I read that beetroot is bad for the muscles. I felt queasy as I ate the stuff. Then there's red meat. That's the Devil's food as well. No more flesh is to pass these lips. There are days when I think the click is about to start again, but it's a false alarm, and I look to one side, and there's just a little sort of *thwock* sound. Not a click as such. I told the quack I have rare bone structures. Hence the click. My neck should be subject to medical research.

Big Sulk

Hello Ivy... Joan here... yes I thought I'd ring you for a change. I bet you're surprised eh?

I wanted to know how Harold and yourself are getting on. Oh, nothing doing? Well you know, the fact is that men sulk, love. They do. I've known plenty of them and I can tell you, from the heart, that they sulk. They can sulk for England, men. The current Mr Hemper has learned, from experience, that sulking does not cut the mustard with yours truly.

But they *can* sulk. I mean by that how they tend to find a hole and slink into it, thinking they're little wounded animals, seeking darkness. Oh yes. You remember my first! Gosh, he once went away to sulk for three days. I almost called out the police. He was found with his Uncle Fred in Dewsbury. They had drunk beer and played darts for four days! Why? Because he wanted to make me suffer after we fell out, and sulking was the way he did it.

Plus, the bombs. If he talks about bombs then he needs some help. He has what they call an obsession. I've been reading about it. I bet his family were in the Blitz. Try to stop him obsessing about being blown up, dear.

Keep a look-out for what Harold does in the garden. Does he have a shed? Yes? Right, there we are. That's where he sulks - pound to a penny. Why don't you shout over the fence one day? Men always have to stalk off somewhere and not be seen. I've seen that over and over again through the years.

This Harold, he's hurting, love. He's lost his mate. He's the lion with no lioness. Knock on his door. Wake him up a bit... oh, I have to go. Mrs Wheatley's at the door, wanting to unload herself about her wayward son, Arthur... he'll end up behind bars, that one... love you! Bye!

Men are very simple really. They need food for the belly and a body to hold at night. Even the strange ones like the one you've chosen are like that, believe me. Be direct with him. No messing around. But first, find out where he sulks. There is always a sulking place, hidden away somewhere.

What I Want

Turns out he's a liar, like all the others.

No, listen, Julie, I'm not saying that. I'm not saying that I want some wonderful, rich boffin! No, I just want somebody to hang around with who says more than what a nice day it is and do I want to have another drink? I mean it's all some ridiculous game isn't it? A guy takes you out. You talk. *He* takes you out again, and you kiss goodnight. *He* takes you out again, and you screw. *He* buys everything. *He* leads the way. *He* decides. You know what I'm saying, Julie, surely?

Yes, your mate, Cynthia, is going to be an artist. I want to paint... something different. I want to paint emotions and prayers and curses... all the things we can't see. Does that make sense?

Well, sorry, I didn't put it very well.

When I come back into the world from college, I want to be distinctive. That's the word. Something rich and famous. Something different from what these suburbs make us into. Mam and Dad, take them for instance... worked hard all their lives, saved up for a fortnight's holiday every August, made Christmas into some damned great feast with kids swarming over hills of presents, overeating and screaming out with joy as they rip open another parcel... no, no, I'm not being unfair! They are perfectly fine. They have been good parents, of course. I just want something different. *Distinctive*, yes, that's not a sin is it? Wanting to be distinctive? I want to design book covers and do illustrations for stories. It won't shake the world, but it's not sitting in a warehouse packing boxes!

Well I thought he was the one... he's a student on the building site. Tallish, tight jeans, fashionable shirts... a student like me. Literature I think. But we've not said much. I'm going to have to talk first. He's shy as well as a liar. Not a good start, no. He's called Andy. I think he's a poet. I'll give him another chance I guess.

Anyway, I'll ring again next week. Roll on the new term! See ya....

What? *The Feminine Mystique.* A book? No, I haven't read it. Betty Friedan wrote it? Oh I see. So she's said that we can't be defined by being wives and mothers... slaves in the kitchen? Well I agree with all that. Does she let us be romantic though? I like being romantic. That's why lads like Andy are always after me. I think that's what I've got – the feminine mystique. Yes, I know you can't buy it in a shop. Course. Yes, I'll read it.

Dr P. Stone,

7, Asphodel Avenue,

Knotworth

Yorkshire

United Kingdom

Dear Both,

For Christ's sake, sort out this yob. Get a pit bull, pay a thug, but put the frighteners on the little toad. Don't make a twit into an ogre. I really can't make it home for Xmas. I nearly wangled it, then fate stepped in. Someone taken ill and I'm needed more than ever. Jomo's asked me to spend the summer holiday with him. His father's a musician and they're into reggae.

I can feel myself changing. Out here there's so much that moves you and pushes you to be more open to life.

Africa IS changing me. I have found a direction. I want to do so much – learn languages, play music, kick the drones! You stirrer, Dad. That good and evil stuff! I put your point to Jomo and the others overheard – we could write a book on it. The consensus is that evil is separated too often – that, in fact, evil is a dark side of God. The local beliefs make him separate, with a domain, rules and attitudes. Keith from Battersea says the bad is genetic and there's a breed of undermen to oppose the strong supermen. But the undermen cheat. The supermen have a tougher time as they think laws are respected. He says the violent stories grab us with this – and how the goody fights back properly!

It's too hot to be intellectual – and I'm swotting up grammar. I keep being asked to explain things about my own language and can't. I need you, Dad, with your Latin. Can you help?

The package was appreciated. Love whodunnits. Any cherry cake?

Love,

Tom

She Spoke

Cynthia spoke to me! She did. She spoke. She still likes me. She's forgiven the fib. In fact she laughed. My heart was in my mouth. I tried to say something but all that came out was gibberish. She must think I'm an idiot. But at least I now know that she's studying art and she likes poetry. Would it be too much to write a poem for her? I'd look too soft in the head. But then, if a poem is honest, if the feeling behind it is honest, then that will come through... surely. I mean, I know that I feel something for her... it's not just that I fancy going to bed with her and that. If I wrote a poem and... no, for Christ's sake, don't be stupid, Andrew!

She is a very special girl. No, she's a woman. I mustn't call her a girl. No, a poem might be pushing things too far. I think the western way is the best. Like the old gunfighters in the cowboy films. You just tell women the facts. You put a glass of wine in front of them, sit down opposite and say, *'You're the woman I been lookin' fer... them lips is meant for nobody but me, woman!'* No, she would most likely slap me.

Mr T. Stone,

Centre 223, Fair Lawns,

Nairobi,

Kenya

Dear Tom,

It was good to hear from you. Shame about the holidays. We have a social life though – Mr. Naven and wife – Denis and Lisa – took us to opera in Nottingham. A trek but we enjoyed it.

I'm in the study again. Sadly, mum had a relapse this morning. I'm writing this to distract myself. If it's gibberish, forgive me. The wind is lashing against the window and I hear the trees bending and creaking as they sough in the gusts. They are so lovely, even in a storm – a constant source of pleasure. It's supposed to be summer, though.

Good to hear about the debate – and I did buy that plane! I've come back to the letter. Update on the yob. There's glass on the wall, barbed wire on the fence and gate heightened. I've spoken to the law but they've no time for this. He's been in the garden again near the hives. He tried to spray paint on the wall. He'd put 'old git' when I disturbed him and he ran. I can move a bit when I want. He's a damned coward.

I refuse to be unnerved by the devil. He's like bloody Caliban, haunting the place. I'll spray him one day.

Tuition, as you say, is always something with a good income. The old Empire might have been a rotten thing, but it did give our mother tongue a certain exchange value! Go for it, son! You were always good with words of course. Look how quickly you mastered French.

Your ambitions are, of course, admirable.

Love,

Dad.

A Lesson

Now, Andy, what you do... I mean what I do when I'm Maori Maleroa... is look fierce. See, your Maori warrior... he pulls a face like. Like this... watch how my tongue comes out and my skin sort of creases... and my eyes flash... see... fierce eh? Scare a bull in a *corrida...* you know us wrestlers, we're like the bulls in the *corridas.* I went once... saw this guy, flapping his rug at the bull. It stamped its feet and snorted at him. It would put the fear of God into most men. Well, us wrestlers, we have to be like that.

But the *haka* you see, it's not all about scaring the enemy. No, it can be to honour the enemy! Yes. Hard for the European to understand. But it makes wonderful show business when you're on the canvas...

We've always had wrestlers in the Slack family. Goes back centuries. Wrestlers and bare-knuckle fighters. I tried that once. Had to pack it in when I saw that I was too slow. I'm a slow mover, you see.

Now, it's good for the crowd. They like exotic. You need to be strange. Exotic. There's Harry from Cleckheaton, he's The Samurai. Then there's my cousin Rodney, he's The Todmorden Tormentor. These names, you see, they stick. Folk remember the names. I mean, you would remember The Maori Maleroa wouldn't you? There you are you see. What I do, I stamp one foot like this... after I've pulled the face and blinked. It's called a Haka. My manager wanted me to be The Hard Haka at first but I didn't like it.

179

For hours before a fight, I'm working on my head. You know, telling myself I'm not Simon Slack. He's gone, the boring little get. No, rising up in me is the man from the South Island, tough as a rhino and deadly as a shark... The Maori Maleroa! I can feel him sort of baking in the oven, so to speak, in here... like if I bang my chest I can rattle him and he'll be coming out, in a killing mood, evil personified, and then by the time I'm in that ring, staring at the opponent like I'm going to eat him, Maleroa has taken over. *Aaaaaargh!*

Don't tell the others about this, will you? It's our secret.

Got any chocolate left, Andy?

Al Back from the Dead with a Bay Mare

Sorry, Paddy. I slipped into that bog by the east road. That's why I look so bad. I know, yes, I look like a monster from the horror films. Well, I'd just been helping Sime with the far wall at number four, and I was going to come back here, when I slipped. Now, it was then I found this fella. It was just wandering around on the lane... broke free from somewhere. Beautiful horse. Oh, a mare is it? Right. A bay mare. Are you going to keep it?

Live behind the hut? But what if it belongs to somebody. Yes, I'll keep *schtum*. Can I go and wash now? Thanks. I look like a character from a science fiction film. Could have drowned you know. It was deep. Only when I crawled out and I saw the horse did I realise I was not dead, and walking in hell.

Yes, give her some of the carrots. There's some sausages left over as well. I don't think she's been treated so well. I can sense something in her... something wrong. No, I wasn't brought up with nags. No, but I'm good with beasts generally. Brought up on a farm. Used to shovel manure.

Anyway, I know you'll look after her... I just think it might be *theft*. Okay, okay. Not a word will leave these lips...

Al Goes Poetic

Ladies and gentlemen, now I always read some of Uncle Albert's poems, and this is my favourite. It's called Memory of a Leeds Tram.

Rattling red monster astride the lines,

Running through my youth

With other joys like Woodbines;

Noisy, gauche, alien, uncouth,

You emerged from yellow city smog

Crackling in like fate.

Shame about Mrs Mason's dog,

Who crossed the line quite late.

Albert's going to have a collection of his poems put together. It'll raise some cash for his beer-money box.

Goodnight, my loves, you've been champion tonight, you have! I'm Al Hinchcliff and I've been telling you about my Uncle Albert.

The Magic of the Hut

Now then, Andy... sandwiches all ready... here you are. Potted meat for Simon, and I added some tomatoes. Now listen to this... your Patrick and I dined last night. Oh yes, in the hut! I bet you couldn't tell, when you walked into the hut this morning, that it was the scene of a romantic dinner? He has the charm of the Irish, that man! He had cleared all the tools and work stuff out of the way, and there was that long table, all bedecked with a white linen cloth. Then there were two glasses and a bottle of white wine, with nice clean plates and soup bowls... the lot! Then guess what? Soft music and Al Bowlly singing away. He knows I love Al Bowlly's voice... such a sad story. He died in an air raid you know, poor Al!

It was all sort of hushed though. He played it very softly. Said nobody had to know we were there. Of course, the lights were turned off and he just had candles. Oh, Andrew! What a night! Be still, my beating heart... Candle-light, soft music, and Patrick talking about the beauties of Galway Bay... he said that when we met again somewhere normal, he would sing *The Fields of Athenry* for me and we could weep so that our clothes were damp!

It was odd, not being able to chuckle and giggle. He said there would be big trouble if he was reported to Barney Rathbone. *'The hut is not a domicile for employees,'* he said, and smiled, impersonating your boss's voice.

We're going out properly next time... somewhere where we can laugh and sing. Oh he's the man I used to know, Andrew, before he went strange. Under stress, you see, he's been under stress.

I put extra treats in his bag there... a bun and a scone! Tell him *Rene is his queeny* - it'll make him laugh.

Wifely Material

You know, these sandwiches, they're the best. Tell them that at the shop, Andy. Tell them that Hooky thinks they make the best cheese and pickle butties this side of the Appalachians. I've been there you know. Oh yes. I used to travel. But I'm not going to moan on about things because... wait for it lads... I think I've found the true wife... she's wife material if ever there was one. French too! She's well, *possibly* French. Not sure yet. She *sounds* French. Her name? Edita. She's called Edita. It's a poem isn't it? It's true, and I'm ecstatic, lads! A beautiful woman and she likes a carrot-top Yorkie with spots! Dreams do come true!

You know what I did? I took her to the poshest restaurant in Forley. It's so foreign nobody knows what cuisine it is. But she liked it. The menu was in French. Edita? She's petite, jet black hair... perfumed like the mystic East. Neat little nose you want to kiss... bit of a stutter, but that could be the language. She has a mole on one cheek. Wears boots with jewels in them. No, Sime, she is not a high-class whore! For God's sake, stop knocking everything in life.

She ordered some kind of steak with a sauce the colour of Heinz Baked Beans and I had a curry. When we finished she put a wet finger on my nose end and said, *'Let's go somewhere where I can kiss you all over your body...'* well, wifely material or what?

No, I know it's not about sex. We clicked. I believe in souls that are meant to be one, like sort of twins

185

only spiritual, you know. We went back to her flat, but her brothers were there. She has three brothers. They all glared at me. I was a bit nervous so I went home. She saw me off, and at the door, she put her hand on my... on my... she put her hand on an intimate place and...

No, Simon, she is not on the game! I'm going to ask Edita to marry me. I shall do it at the band concert in Forley Park on Sunday. I think a good trombone solo softens any heart.

Right Paddy, back to work. But tell the shop about the wonderful sandwiches, Andy lad.

Flowers

What ARE you doing, Patrick? It looks like another flower-bed. Aubretias? Saxifrage? We're not a garden shop are we? You remember that I told you about the boss - his letter about the hut? Well, he won't like this. Look, Paddy, think about a building site. That's what we are: a building site. Now that's a shifting thing, it comes and goes. It's not a place where you put down roots. A flower-bed seems to suggest that this hut is a kind of home. I know it's to make the place a bit more welcoming, yes. I see what you're saying. Point is, old mate, I don't want it to seem welcoming. It's a hut. It's five sides with a roof and a door at the front. It's planks, boards, flimsy stuff. Not a home, Paddy. Not a home. Now, if you spent your time laying bricks or plastering that wall at number fifteen, that would be important... your dinner hour? Well okay, you did it in your dinner hour. Fine. But still, I mean, they're going to be taken out aren't they? Left behind and that. It's not there to last, that bed. Right, right, so it's beauty and beauty is for a moment, yes, that's very Irish and very poetic, Paddy... no, I'm not being offensive. It's a compliment.

But the problem is you see, that the hut is not a permanent thing, is it? You're giving a lot of time and energy to something that's going to be taken apart. If you could put all that graft into something like the drives on the Crescent... you and Al are doing that tomorrow by the way. The wagon's here at ten. But please, no more flowers round the hut - agreed?

187

Dr. P. Stone,

7, Asphodel Avenue,

Knotworth,

Yorkshire,

United Kingdom

Dear Both,

Get the law onto the pest now. He's damaged property, threatened you, and caused anxiety and stress. Mum, make Dad see some sense. The bad blood must have reached here. A youth was shot a few miles away. Drugs they say. Let's hope things don't escalate. We had the law here to sort out some threats from his relatives apparently. What matters is that I'm getting somewhere. The Head says that he's getting good reports so I may even make a career of teaching after all. I have tended to dip into things, I know. But it's different now.

Mum, take things easy, please. I'm such a long way from you and I worry. I'm going to be home soon, I'll make sure of that.

Holiday soon – take it easy.

Love,

Tom.

Cramp

Cramp last night lads. Bloody cramp! I just turned over, perfectly fine, and then it struck. I thought only footballers had cramp. Well, how wrong can you be! My big leg muscle gave me agony. Never known a pain like it. I shot out of bed and hopped across the ruddy room. Woke up the missus. She screamed at me: did I need an ambulance, was it my ticker again? I was whooping like a flipping Sioux warrior. So she gets out of bed, pushes me back on the bed... I thought ey up, what does she want? I'm not up to them tricks, not with my constitution. Then she massages my leg, sort of pushes up the heel. Could have been a nurse, my missus. That's why I wed her. Well, it worked. But I've never known pain like it, lads. Never. She said I was dehydrated and I should drink less coffee. Should have been a nurse, she should.

But here I am, drinking coffee anyway, with some true friends. You know, Barney, Paddy, Sime, Andy... you're proper mates. True friends. With a man like me, weak and handicapped as I am, true friends are more than gold. I can unburden myself to you any time, about anything, and you never complain. You've stopped teasing me as well. You patiently listen. It's wonderful. It's a very rare thing, being in this hut with you blokes. Particularly when I think... I mean, I think... I may not have long left.

No, seriously, this cramp, it's a sign that parts are freezing up, starting to wear away. It's right! The doctor said so... the new doctor. He's got more letters after his name than there are in the Russian alphabet. The body you see, the body... is like an engine, and it wears away, it grinds down... cramps are a sign that you're not long for this earth. A cramp is a sort of final warning. The body wants to tell you something crucial, you know. You've seen the footballers, keeling over in agony... well, that's cramps. Like I've got now. It is nothing to giggle about like schoolkids, believe me!

You can laugh, Simon Slack, you can laugh... you're still a damned good friend though.

The Letter

Now then, young Andrew, the sandwiches are all ready. Can I ask a favour as well, lad? See this one here? This is for Paddy. Patrick I should say. I should call him Patrick. What do you think this little note in here is all about? Yes, I've asked to meet him. We used to walk out, and we were quite close. About a year ago it was... he went all strange on me. I thought we were going steady at one time. Anyway, if you could make sure he gets this, and that none of the other lot see the note. Can you do that, love?

You're a smasher. You remind me of a young man I went out with when I was twenty. Oh yes, lovely eyes, like you. We both worked in a home. Funny how those places are called *homes* don't you think? They're anything but homes in truth. I worked with this young man – Derek he was called – well, he was my first boyfriend. There was this old man. He'd been hurt in the first war. Gas. Bad lungs. He was funny in the head. Used to grope me. Showed me his private parts. Well I was scared of him, so I asked Derek to do the lifting and bath the old man, that sort of thing. He did. So I could avoid the old beggar. Well one night, when I went on a night shift, Derek wasn't there. He was poorly. I went to the old man's room to get him in the bath... he was very small and light, all shrivelled up he was, skin and bones. Anyway I went into his room, and saw his little face in the bed. I went to him, all nervous like... but not a word was spoken. I got up close, and he wasn't moving.

You've guessed it, Andy. He was my first corpse. All grey his face was. Cold, like a bar of lard, he was to touch. But you know, his room – he had a small table, a chair and a few magazines, all about cars and military stuff. Nothing else apart from his wardrobe with a few trousers and shirts. Nobody ever came to see him.

Is that where we all end up, Andy? I think it is. So you know what's most important? To have somebody to love... somebody who loves you. If you find that person, take hold of 'em and treat 'em like royalty. Listen to this daft old woman, Andy... she's got some wisdom under all the small talk. Have you found that person, lad?

Tell Patrick I'm saving a sandwich cake for when we meet up.

Mr T. Stone,

Centre 223, Fair Lawns,

Nairobi,

Kenya

Dear Tom,

I know it's pathetic, but this young villain is coming and staring at me. It's just that I can see him across the road every night. All he does is watch. It's not going to bother me. I just sense a presence, I mean. He can't find a way into the house, only by the gate, that's still the weak point.

But Phil, the trees – you should see them. They are so lovely. There's no land on earth with trees like ours. The oak and the ash and the bonny rowan trees and all growing high in the north country. I'm singing to you again, son. I see you when I look on the lawn, toddling as you used to, pointing at birds. The first words you spoke were 'Darling starling' *– first proper words, if you see what I mean.*

I am a fortress. I am a rock. What is built on me is solid. Nothing shall pass – not the ghetto blasters, the rowdies, the eyes from the dark, everything that is smut. I stand against these. Son, come home. Bring your bloody Jomo, your grammar book – just bring yourself. Everything is so still. There is that iron silence after a storm.

There's a lot of coming and going with the building down the street - I mean, they're finishing the estate and they're a few hundred yards from me but I can still hear the noise. Roll on the autumn, when they're supposed to be finishing it all. Mind you, I read deep into the night. You know what I'm like - always got about six books on the go at the same time. I read by mood, of course, and I think you do the same.

Toilet Refuge

She's over there, that Baker woman - she's never going to give in! Maybe I should show my face, go and confront the facts. I mean after all, that's my kid in her belly. Oh why the hell has this had to happen to me? I mean how daft is this - me in a toilet, in a half-finished semi, in a desolate part of Yorkshire, squatting below the window, being invisible until she buggers off.

I feel such a coward. Fact is, I *am* a coward. I have to change. It's not fair, what I do. Come on man, get a grip. You can't keep running all your life. But... but if I go out there and face her, take responsibility.... oh God that's the word. Responsibility. Puts the shivers all through me, that word. Gives me the screaming ab-dabs! Responsibility. It means bills, duties, jobs, doing as you're told... that's not me.

Oh hell's bells! One of the lads has bloody told her where I am! She's coming this way. By heck, I think I can tell from the way she walks that's she's well on in the preggy way. What are you going to do, lad? You're in a fix this time. She's shouting my name! Christ! Keep your head down, Sime... head down.

She'll get bored. She'll go. Thing is, what if it's *not* yours? What if she's put her favours around a bit and slept around... and she's taking me for a sucker? What then? She can't get into this place anyway. She'll go away.

The Feminine Mystique

Julie... hi! I've not got long... got to be at work. I just thought I'd tell you that I read that book. The mystique. I've been persuaded! Oh yes. I'm going to exude mystique. It's right isn't it – I mean, you need to be a woman free from all that slavery, and we have to stop showing adverts where women are in the kitchen. Women can be doing sports or be models and actresses and that... but in everyday life they need to be mysterious. Men need to be puzzled by us. That right? Well, this Andy, he thinks I'm full of mystique, and I love it. 'Bye Julie... be mysterious!

Running a Book

There's an update on *Dick Diver,* boys. Not too late to stick a bit more on. I know the last one didn't work out, but this is different. This one is a world-beater. I have it on the best horseflesh authority... how about another small investment from you, Simon? No? How about you, Gordon? Well, look, he's been seen in the gallops by the man from the *Mirror*. Fleet as the wind, he writes, fleet as the wind. Now, he's seven to one. What about another fiver each? I've got forty quid on now... got him at twenty to one... two months back,. Inside knowledge, you see, inside knowledge. Our Declan's boy, he's a stable lad at the Curragh. Says he'll lead all the way.

The latest reports from the gallops assure us that the horse is covering the ground like a missile. I kid you not, this is a classic winner. His coat has a sheen to dazzle you and his every little move on the turf suggests class and style. His name is going to be in the record books, believe me.

Oh boys, boys, can you see old Paddy now, on that beach in Grenada, lovely spot... feet up on a chaise longue and a butler fetching a pint of porter... some lovely woman asking if I need anything... can you see that, boys? Behind me, the blue-tinged mountains and before me the still Caribbean and the clouds nowhere to be seen. They're all over Ireland as usual... or over bloody Yorkshire!

I'm running my own book now boys for that race... four days away now. Three to one the favourite... but get your spondulix on *Dick Diver* and think of your fat wallets as you trot down the boozer next week. Empty your pockets now boys. He moves like the wind... he opens his nostrils, pounds the earth with his feet, and he's a ground-eater, that one. A ground-eater I tell you, lads.

Go on, Say it

It's not difficult. Everyone you talk to agrees that women like you to be direct, up-front, say what you mean. So, what you say is: *'You're Cynthia aren't you? Well I'm Andy. I think we're both students. Would you like to come out to dinner with me?'* No, maybe not dinner... maybe the flicks. But then, I need to be wearing smarter clothes. I'm wearing an orange tee-shirt, sandy-coloured Army and Navy Stores working pants and shoes with floppy soles. Add to that the fact that I'm covered in muck, and you have... failure of course. So, imagine I'm in a suit... my one dark blue suit, and a white shirt with the flowery tie. Here we go: *'Hello Cynthia. I'm Andy. We're both students, and I'd like to take you out some time....'*

No, not some time... now! *'Hello Cynthia... what a lovely name you have...'* no, that's shit.

The thing is, she's different. She's not like other girls. She wears these weird clothes... like they wore back before the war and that. She has perfume. Maybe she's a cut above me?

Dear Irene,

How lovely to receive your letter. As you are the only person who knows my little secret, I can tell you that if you come along to the hut at seven on Friday, I'll have the kettle on, and you can bring some custard tarts if you like. Then, I have to be careful of course - can't make any noise. It's supposed to be locked up for the weekend and left empty of course. If Barney knew I'd get the heave-ho and I'd be home again tossing hay for my brother.

Oh Renee, how sweet it is that you're giving me a second chance! I know I was a bit of a bastard before, but in my defence I was under stress, worrying about my old mother's condition, and then there was the bug raging through Jim's stables. I know a man's not to give airy-fairy excuses but when I threw the wobbly and had the big sulk, it was down to the stress and the gargle. But I'm on the wagon now apart from the odd pint at the Club, just to be sociable, you understand.

Come along then. We'll have the place to ourselves. You know what - we could have a game of cards. Not Strip Poker of course. Nothing untoward. (I'm joking!) No, it'll be like our own little house. You see, I've put my own imprint on this hut. It's my very own, not like any other hut in the land. I've even carved my name on a square of plywood and stuck it over the corner where the kettle is. The only item missing in the place is yourself. I don't mean by that the reference to you as an item. Far from it. You are something above the ordinary of the earth, my love.

I should point out, Rene, with reference to any future we might have together, that as I am living in the hut, I am spending nothing at all on digs! I've saved up a tidy sum, and it's destined to ride on the back of a certain thoroughbred called Dick Diver *next week. When that comes in – notice I said when, not if - I'll be the Lord of the Manor with money to chuck around like Rothschild, so I will. I want you to share my new life, Rene. I know we can't wed like, as you're still tied up with that drunkard from Manchester. But we can be pals and adventurers, right? What do you say?*

You and I, we could be such a happy couple. I can see us together, living life to the full. Can you see that too?

See you Friday my darlin' beauty.

Paddy

Mr T Stone,

Centre 223, Fair Lawns,

Nairobi,

Kenya

Dear son,

July now. I ought to say that I wrote a letter but I'm not sure I sent it. Can't seem to get going – the summer blues. I'm gazing on the lawn. The birds are still raiding the fatballs. A robin has adopted me – or am I just wishing that?

    I did tell you about your Aunt Gina? She's been very ill, and I'm afraid she passed away two days ago. You remember you used to play board games with her? She loved you. I'll miss her very much. As for your mum, she's not well either of course. We have to live with it. Every muscle in her body seems to ache most days. She has to go to bed every afternoon, and the radio is a God-send.

    Anyway, I still have the restless youth out there, and I will not give him the satisfaction of knowing that he's annoying me. He's just a little rat. Of course, the worst thing is I know he's there. The eyes are in the trees after dark. It's when I go out for the coal, I can see the yellow eyes staring from behind the bough where I hung the feeder. I can make out the legs, the grey trousers. He's watching me but I have to go on. There have always been eyes. I've always believed in fences and walls but they can't keep everything out. What was it Antony said? 'Let Rome in Tiber melt... here is my space.'

Yes, they can watch, and my hives will stand and my bare trees will be lovely, and the voices of my young lovers will always be heard in the corners of my own garden, my own place.

I'm going to sit in the back room and read my War and Peace *tonight, but raise a glass to your aunt.*

Yours,

Father.

The Going was too Soft

What can I say? I'm absolutely destroyed by the race. I mean, it rained and rained solid, for two days before the meeting. It was just too soft. See, his breeding says it all. He was bred to go like a rocket, as long as the ground is hard. He loves to hear his feet rattle, does *Dick Diver.* I hope to God above that you didn't have too much on his back. What? What? Well, Simon, I said be steady, hold back a little... no, I'm not a bloody liar. No, I never said put your mortgage on the thing! I never did, surely. Did I, Al? I did? Oh my Aunt Carmel and by the Seven Holy Men of Ringsend, I beg your pardon lads. If I ever said put a stack on him, I'm most grievous sorry.

What can I say? The ground was like a bog. Any bag of bones could have won the race if it acted on a bog. The quality horses need proper ground. That's a fact, an equine fact, lads. I'm not flannelling you, I swear.

Who the hell would know all that pissin' rain would come sheeting down? I mean I thought old Ireland was wet but stab me vitals, this bloody Yorkshire takes the absolute biscuit. I mean, does the sun *ever* get through the gloom in this benighted place? They say Ireland has rain, but there's nothing like this God-forsaken country.

I can only say how sorry I am, and I promise that the next tip will be a corker. What? Oh Gordon, come on, what do you mean? You'll never listen to my opinions again? And you a man with not long left on this earth... sorry, I shouldn't have said that. I think you're being so brave, old friend, so brave. Isn't he being courageous, lads? Yes, there you are, we love you Gordon, we love you, old mate. Now it's not every day you hear a man talk like that in this stiff upper lip country you English inhabit!

I'm saying this because we had a talk, me and the lads, and though we tease you a bit, we know you've had a lousy time and we want to cheer you up, give you a treat. You need a holiday, old lad.

Now, what we did was pass the hat round for you, old mate, and we've raised quite a bit and we'd like you and your dear mother to have a little holiday on us... Barney, do you have the box of donations there? Thanks. Now, Gordon, there's a considerable amount of spondulix in here, as the boss himself put his hand deep in his overalls... so have a bloody good time. And I'm so sorry about the nag. The damned rain!

The Lady in the Audience

Paddy, you'll not believe it... there I was, at the Working Men's Club in Cackbury, and I asked for a member of the audience to come on stage, you know, for a little dialogue I do... well this young lady comes out. Paddy... she was beautiful! I thought that I'd had my last chance with the ladies, now I'm forty five like, but well, turns out she's a *groupie*. A groupie... you know. Like these lasses what follow the bands, hang around the stage door... offer their, their *services* if you see what I mean? No, they're not whores, Paddy. Well this one isn't. She Katy and she's like Marilyn Monroe... a stunning blonde... and she thinks my Uncle Albert stories are great! She does! Here's me thinking my career has gone down the pan. She's really funny. Naturally funny, Paddy. Another thing – she's Irish. Yes, I know you Irish are naturally humorous... very creative. Well that's Katy. You'll have to come and see me... she's going to be in the act, like.

See This Bayonet

Here you are again. More rain. Well I looked at the sky and I thought, I bet those lads are in the Club today, so I'll take something to show them. I know it's not pleasant, but then war never is, and war has been my profession. This, my friends, is the bayonet I had in the Big Push. It's going in my book, all this, particularly the time I used it to save my neck. Hand-to-hand combat it was. We all knew the day would come... mine's a pint of bitter please... we knew the day would come when we would have to use them, on an actual person that is. It's all very well screaming blue murder and charging at a sack full of rice, but to stick a man's guts – even Kraut – well that's another matter.

Sit down, sit down, pull up your chairs lads. It was a foggy day in France. Clouds had pressed down on us. The sun had been pushed out. It was a day when there was to be nothing that God up in Heaven wanted to see. It was a day for the Devil's handiwork, and it involved thrashing about with these things... deadly blades of steel!

I thought this would brighten your day. Blokes can't resist the old flash of steel, eh? Some think we should forget those old times, but when you've been in the thick of it, everything sort of lingers in the mind, you see?

The Proposal

Well lads, as I've been munching that bun, I've been dying to tell you what happened with Edita. Yes, Andy, I did ask her. I asked for her hand. It was just as the brass band was taking the applause for their last number. The noise subsided, and in that moment of peace I held her arm gently, looked into her eyes and asked her to be my fourth wife. No, Paddy, she said no. The problem was that she knew nothing of the other three. I'd kept *schtum* about that. It had all gone sadly wrong. I can't understand it. I had even sung *The Galway Shawl* for her at one point. You know, '*She wore no jewels, no costly diamonds...*' all that stuff. If she had said yes, I planned to sing *You are my Heart's Delight* as well. But no, you should have seen her face as she said 'Fourth?'

The thing is, you see, that a woman from the Eastern countries, well, she's Slavic. Now Slavs are a passionate race. Easily moved to passion, oh yes. I have to treat her with care. One wrong word and zoom... she's gone! Whimsical is the word, and so a man has to be whimsical in his own way... how do you mean I talk some bollocks? Simon, do we have to have the tone lowered in this way? There's enough scum in the world without us adding to it. I'm not talking bollocks. I'm talking romance. Something your average Northerner needs to understand if he's to win the heart of a good woman... or a good man if that's his taste.

Still, Edita has been put off me. She sensed a rogue. A lothario. I should have kept my mouth shut. Silence has its place.

Well, I could try again. But I guess she's told the brothers. I think they're a mafia. I think I might be a marked man. Why did I come clean? Me and my big gob!

One o'clock. Yes Paddy. Finish off number nine. I obey your command. I'm off now.

Dear Jim,

You will never believe it. I have acquired a horse – a lovely bay mare. I'd say she's around fifteen. Oh good Lord, no, she's never going to race. Though you do get horses her age winning little chases sometimes. No, she just turned up. She must belong to somebody of course. Anyway, I'm building a little lean-to at the back for her. Well if the law comes calling, looking for her, then of course I'll say I'm taking care... yes, I know I could still be charged with something. England is like that. They'll have an offence for staring too long at a blue sky I suppose. But there you are. I have a horse, just to take care of you see. The shit will come in handy for the wee garden I'm slowly developing. What do you mean, when it dies? She's pretty healthy. I inspected her. Teeth are good. Legs are sound. She's a touch barmy, but then all horses are. No, I'm going to ride her every so often, out into the fields by Brighouse. There are fields in Knotforth too, of course. She's probably from one of the farms down the valley. Now look, between you and me, I'm thinking of her as mine already. She feels *like mine.*

Anyway, save up your cash for the big race. We're going to be made this time, brother mine. Yes, give my love to cousin Mary and to the kids. Bye Jim.

The End in Sight

Now lads, you can see, as well as I can, that the end of July approaches fast. Now, we're not going to complete by the last day of July. I've managed to persuade the company management to let us have until 26 August to finish. By six o'clock on that day, there has to be no more trowels to fill and no more concrete to lay down. Savvy? That's more than generous I think. I explained it was all down to the weather. If we had been working in Rome or Athens then it might have been different. But we're squashed between Leeds and Bradford and it pisses it down on six days out of seven. Now we can't say it's been a tough summer can we Paddy? I mean you've put on two stone, old pal, sitting in that hut, eating and supping. Now let's give it some welly and meet that deadline, right? The end is in sight.

We're living in funny old times, lads, and there's labour problems up one street and bombs dropping in another. Your lovely Ireland is going to explode, I reckon, Paddy. The world wants to blow itself apart I reckon. But in the Asphodels there will be family homes. Right? Lovely, safe and strong family homes, where little Johnny can play safely and little Mary can do her hopping and skipping without fear of the garage falling down. These are proper houses, built by blokes like us. That reminds me, Gordon, can you tighten that side gate at number twenty four? Thanks. Just the hinges and that. The toilet door at number twelve needs a better lock. That's your job, Sime. Thanks, now let's get to work. The concrete mixer comes in an hour. And see... no bloody rain today.

The Big Moment

Hi... I'm Andy by the way. You're Cynthia aren't you? A half of bitter please, and some cheese and onion crisps. Thanks. I was wondering... I was wondering... yes, I am a student. I study English Literature... in Wales. I'm in Wales. Aberystwyth. Yes they speak Welsh all around you. Sometimes you go in a shop, and they serve the Welsh people before you... rude yes. They really want to keep their language. You sort of respect that yes... oh, so I was wondering if maybe some time... oh, you study art? Somebody said that, yes. Been talking about you? Course I have. I think you're very, very... oh you want to be a book illustrator? That's wonderful. One day you could do the pictures to go with my poetry... yes I write poetry. I was wondering if... well, I like Wordsworth and Tennyson... we're studying them. But my favourite is T.S.Eliot... oh you like *The Waste Land* as well? That's great! One night I sat up for ages, writing this long poem... twenty four pages I wrote, stayed up until three in the morning. Then the next day, sitting at the kitchen table, I read it through and it made no sense. I'd written it in a trance... it was too much like *The Waste Land*... what? You illustrated *The Waste Land*? That's terrific. Can I see it? I was wondering... oh yes, bring it then. I won't take it home, no. We could read it one dinner time. We both get an hour I think. Oh, I live north of Leeds... you live where? Oh, Keighley? Brontë country! You lucky thing!

I was wondering if you would... oh I know, the Brontës, fabulous. Emily. She's your favourite! Mine too. I wrote an essay on her last term. Look, I was just wondering if you would... you would? That's great.

There's a film... *In Like Flint*. Friday night? Great! We'll go straight from here then. I'll bring a change of clothes. A wash? Well I can get a wash at Irene's place. She's the lady with the bakery... smashing lady. We talk a lot.

Friday then. It's a date. I think you're lovely. I just wanted to say that, so you're, you know, clear about where we stand. Well, where we stand is that I think you're fab.

Dear Barney,

I never thought I would be writing again about that damned hut of yours, but now I have been told that there is a horse tethered behind it! What is going on there? I trust that Mr Lanagan cut down on the flowers and the painting etc. I trust that he also changed his attitude to the yard and the purpose of the place? Well, if this horse is anything to do with him, I want it removed immediately. There is no place for animals in one of our materials and support bases! I mean, for heaven's sake, what will people think? Could I urge you to have a meaningful conversation with Mr Lanagan and ascertain the reason for the horse being there?

I would also like to add that, as my informant had reported, there appears to be some kind of lean-to extension behind the site shed, and the horse in question appears to reside in this, and that there is, allegedly, a basket of hay slung over one side of the lean-to extension.

We have to consider our reputation, as well as the functional, workaday matters, in the construction industry. What I mean is that we could be an object of ridicule if it gets out that our site shed is something akin to a farm stable or a domestic villa.

I know I can rely on you to resolve this.

Nigel Bentham-Caldwell

P.S. Couldn't this horse be given to the local farmer? I hope to God it does not belong to such a man, and has been purloined by your Irishman.

The Rival

Sit down lads. No, fine day, but I won't keep you. Mine's a pint of bitter. I'm almost at the end of my tale. It will all go in the book, you see. Everything I've been telling you will all go in the book, and you'll all have a copy coming your way, signed of course. There's only one little glitch in the way of success. Another damned old sweat is writing his memoirs as well! Yes, Teddy Armless is self-publishing the history of his life with the regiment! Damned cheek of the man! You know, in this world of sin there is always some rival. There's a rival for the lady of your heart; there's a rival for that top job; there's a rival at the bar when it's last orders... and there's a bloody rival when you turn your talents to the pen. So here is the bugger, lost his arm in the Boer War. He's now eighty two for Christ's sake, and his daughter is publishing the book for him. The cheek!

I have to say the man is out of line. I mean, he was a damned cook! He never fired a shot in anger, and he only wielded a knife when he sliced meat! The outrageous cheek of the man! Let me tell you the truth about Teddy Armless. His real name was Cuddy. Now I ask you - a man called Teddy Cuddy – it's almost cuddly teddy don't you think? Well this man shamed the colours. At the slightest hint of trouble he was to be found behind the thunderbox smoking a fag. If there was a whisper about an advance, he sorted out a blighty by cutting part of a finger off. By 1918 he was down to two stubs on the left hand. Funny how bits of shrapnel kept hitting the fingers of the same hand hey?

He was born a poltroon and graduated to yellow-bellied funk-ridden failure. The red berets searched high and low for the man when he was nowhere to be seen after the affair of the dodgy sausages. Oh yes, we all asked questions about exactly what meat was used for those bangers. Let me tell you lads... another pint? I will do, yes. Let me tell you, that man could fade into the background in two seconds. Moved like a hunted rabbit, he did. Like a shadow. Teddy Shadow would have been a perfect name for the blighter.

So he's having his memoirs printed, and you know what he's calling the book? He's calling it *The Unofficial General*! Then as a subtitle he's got, *If only they had listened to Private Cuddy on the Western Front...* Damned cad he is. If he wasn't so aged I'd call him out. Lives in a bungalow in Medcaster with a slinky woman doing for him. Well I could do for him given half a chance.

Cheers lads... nice day. No rain. You can get back to the bricks and mortar eh?

Katy and Albert

Paddy, you'll never guess. She's now officially part of the act. Oh yes, Katy is wonderful. They loved her in Pudsey and again in Packwell, they were in fits of laughter... yes of course I'm pleased. She has this smashing routine where she does a string of Irish characters... what a laugh! She flits around the stage like a butterfly. Quick-witted or what! I mean the jokes just stream out of her. The thing is, I think I love her, Paddy. She has mesmerised me, mate.

Oh yes, we're called *Katy and Albert* now.

Pulmonary Summat

What a ruddy horrible morning! I'll join you lads, if you don't mind. Oh, there was a bloke looking for you, Sime. Mr. Dinchop he called himself. Where are you going? Do you owe him some brass then? Anyway, I don't want to ruin your day, lads, but I saw the quack yesterday... new one... he was Scottish. They are the best in the world aren't they- the Scots doctors? Edinburgh... teeming with quacks, top quality. Well he looked at my case file and he said he had to have assistance carrying it in from the filing cabinets. Cheek!

Well, you know I've been complaining about my breathing? It only turns out that I've got pulmonary whatsit. Yes! I can't remember the second word but *pulmonary* means lungs, I think. He was spot on. I've been so bad that my breathing has been sounding like a hacksaw on metal. As for the sputum... bright green! Let me tell you something, boys. Never, ever have anything like a pulmonary whatsit. You feel as though you're waiting in the chamber next to the morgue! You do, that's a fact. When God gave me this body, he was having a laugh. Having a laugh...

'I'm trying to eat my dinner, Gordon!'

Sorry, sorry. I didn't think.

Cap in Hand

Hello Joan... I'm ringing you back now! You were right... he's had a big sulk. He turned up at my door last night, wearing a good suit and a hang-dog expression. He reminded me of Stan Laurel. He said he was sorry, and that thoughts in his head were getting the better of him but that now he was back to his cheerful self again, and would I go out for a drink with him? Let me tell you, I was staggered! *'Get your best frock on,'* he said, *'and come for a drink.'* I didn't know whether to be mad at him, or to just go with the flow... so yes I went with the flow and we went down to The Peacock. By heck, there was a turn on, a right good singer. He was like a Yorkshire Sinatra, he was. Harold bought me gin and limes, told me tales, cracked jokes, and the time flew by.

Now, walking him... and we had drunk a few beers and gins, you must remember... he took hold of my hand and he lifted it to his face and he kissed it, all gentle like... there was just moonlight. He kissed my hand and he said, *'Ivy Carver.... you're a special lady... only the second special lady I've ever known... and you're my good friend.'*

Joan, his words are engraved on my heart! I'm in tears now, only thinking of them. I can see him and hear the way he spoke those words, as I speak to you now. I'm not kidding you, Sis, it was like a scene from a romantic picture... it could have been Humphrey Bogart, not Harold Mond!

Yes, he did sulk... I was mad at him. But I said nothing about that. Should I have said something? You mean, you would have said something? A piece of your mind? Oh I couldn't be mad at him, Sis. I never had a happier time than last night. I kid you not.

I can hear him now, through the wall, singing. He sings the old songs... you know, the ones from the dance bands and the jazz groups... he did go off and brood a bit, but the man lost his wife, Sis. He was left alone... like I was, yes. But men are softer than us. They need looking after. They're like big kids aren't they?

You have to go? Right well, be happy for me... yes?

In Like Andy

Julie, he took me to see a film! Oh my God, it was a man's film... all fists and guns! I hated it, but I wanted to show willing. He was shy, Andy was. Oh yes, but that's so sweet, don't you think? He's never taken a woman out. You can tell. I could feel him shaking, and when he spoke, he almost stuttered. Oh you know what, though, he's got a brain alright! He talked about poetry, about foreign films, about Beethoven and Mozart. He wants to be a poet and be read by what he calls *the masses.* No, he's not got a God complex! I don't think so, anyway. He's just full of ideals and dreams, like me. But please, please let him not take me to any more films with macho men and soft-headed women!

He asked me out again... of course I said yes. I hinted at dinner. We can have a real talk then, instead of just chuckling at the daft dialogue and the hairstyles!

I Know Nothing

A horse, you say? A bay? Well I wouldn't know. You see, mister, I spend all my time in the hut here. My job, see, to care for the hut. If there was a horse ambling by, I wouldn't see it. Ask in the shop. Ask Mrs Kent, the widow lady. She sees everything that goes on around Knotforth. Yes, give me your phone number. If I see a horse I'll ring you straight off, my friend. 'Bye.

Believe me, if a grand horse such as the one you describe came this way, I'd grab him for you, sir. You can depend on me.

What do you mean, Andy, no, I'm not breaking the law. You see that there old man that just came asking the questions? Now he was not a fit man to be in charge of horses. She's better with me. Thank God she didn't do her whinny while the man was here. No, I'm speaking true, Andy. The man was wrong. You only had to look at him to see the brutal streak in him. Did you not read his face? The fissog of a savage I tell you, Andy lad. A savage. I can read people's mugs the same way I read a horse's face. Yes, it's true. It's all in the eyes and the movement of the mouth and the tongue. He was a feckless ne'er-do-well I'll bet you my last sou! No, she's better to me, is my Golden Girl. Yes, of course I've given her a name. You have to. Golden Girl. I'm riding her out at the weekend. I have plans.

I feel as though I've done a noble deed. In fact, I have. I've done a noble deed for a noble animal, so I have.

The Dark Continent

Hello, son... it's me, your dad! Bet that's a shock hey? I decided to ring. Letters are all very well, but I wanted to hear your voice. How are you doing? Oh, travelling again! You should write all about it... I mean you're doing some wonderful things out there. Don't worry about not sending letters. I know how circumstances tend to take over when you're away from civilization... I mean, you are in the dark continent! Did you ever read Conrad's *Heart of Darkness*? Marvellous book... I do recommend it.

Oh, yes, Gina. Of course, yes. We were very close as kids. I'm so glad you remember her well. She always spoke kindly of you... oh the little criminal! He's gone, thank God. It's so quiet here now... except for the day when the builders are here. But I'm told that they finish and bugger off very soon... you've got what? A rash? Well you had all the jabs. Have you been anywhere different? Not been in any squalid sort of place, have you? Oh right... well get it checked out, right?

Mum says a big kiss comes your way every morning.

You have to go? Well you will write, won't you? Promise? Goodbye, son.

Promise

Worry not. We will do it in time and I'll get that bonus. First week in August. Yes, I promise. Like I said, it's two thousand. Look, my love, that week in France is going to happen. With two grand we can do Paris. No, I know my promises have not generally worked out. I know that. But this time, you and me... well, we are off to gay Paree darlin.'

What? Look, it's on paper, in print. It was agreed last November. They've been good to me. They know that in Barney's hands, a good job is done, and it's done on time. We go back a long way, me and this firm. I ought to have shares in it.

I'm going to say the tenth of August. It will all be sorted and signed off by that date. I'm not giving in on this now. We have to keep to that date. I've put it on every calendar, in red ink and underlined.

Yes, yes, of course I know. Yes, we've not had a proper holiday since 1969. Do you think I don't know that, chuck? My mother went with us, of course I remember. But this time it's just you and me. Think about the Arc de Triomphe. Think about the cafes and the dancin' girls! We're just about there, my love, just about home!

Two thousand smackers. Money in our pockets. I know we've never had cash. Yes, easy come and easy go. How many times have you said that? Well, not this time, I promise.

We're going to meet that deadline. I have a good bunch of lads under me. You met Paddy and Simon at that do, remember? Yes, the Irish chap, and the young one. Did they swear? Surely not!

I have to go now. The brick lorry's here. Big kisses. Big kisses... gay Paree!

Harold in Hiding

Joan... I'm so glad you're in. I had to give you a call. It's Harry... I did as you said and I went round to knock on his door, ready to invite him for a chat and a drink at that new pub in Knotforth centre. Well, Joan, what a shock I had! I suppose I shouldn't have gone in, but the door was half open so... well, I went in, slow and steady. There was poor lighting. I called his name. *'Harold,'* I called,*' are you here?'* There was no sound at all. I froze and listened, waiting a few seconds so I could hear anything. If a towel dropped off a rail in the bathroom, I would have heard it.

But there was nothing. No sound. I went into the front room. Everything was in place. Then to the best room, where he has his big table set, for the visitors he never has... then to the back room. Well, there was a shock! It was packed to the rafters with stuff. Everything the man collects was in there. In one corner, and down one side, there were books, hundreds of them. I went to see what they were... well they were all about bombs and weapons, and lots about Russia. I wondered if he spoke Russian. A little voice inside me asked if he might be a Russian spy? But that was daft, surely.

There were stacks of things, many were toys. There were toy railway things, you know. Then there were boxes of pottery. They looked very old. Anyway, just as I was turning around, I heard a noise. It seemed to come from under the floorboards. Then I remembered that of course, he had a cellar, like me.

I shouted again. I shouted louder, calling out his name. There was no answer, but I heard a shuffling noise down in the cellar. The door at the top of the steps was half open. I listened for the sound again. I was sure it was rats. I get rats, you see. I imagined dozens of the little blighters, running around, down in the dark. But I had to get down there and look. I had to be sure. I've read in the paper that rats walk along by a wall, and they leave a line of sweat or water. I saw a light switch, and turned it on. There was just one bulb down there. All it did was light up enough to see shadows.

I took a few steps. They creaked. I froze again and listened. Then out of the dark, I heard someone sobbing. Down I went, going to the place where the sobbing came from. Well, Joan, what a sight! There was Harold, crouched in a corner, hunched up, with one arm stretched out towards me, and in his hand he had a gun. It was a revolver.

'Stop! Who are you? Who are you, in my home? Get out! Get out I say!'

Joan, I thought my last day on earth had arrived. My heart pumped up so that I felt it in my throat. His eyes were staring, like the madmen you see on these horror films. I kept saying, *'It's me, Ivy. It's Ivy from next door... put the gun down!'*

'Ivy', he said. He repeated it a number of times and then he seemed to stop the sobbing, which was going on all the time. *'Ivy... from next door?'* He dropped the gun. You know what I did, Joan? I knelt down, squatting next to

him, and I wrapped my arms around him. In fact, I tumbled next to him, still hugging him, and I kept saying, *'It's fine now, Harry... there's nothing to fear!'*

'They're not here are they? They've not dropped their bombs on us?' He was shivering so much I thought his teeth were going to rattle, like what happens when you're out in the cold too long.

Well, Joan, poor man. What? Yes, after a while, he came round. It must have been half an hour later, I was making him some tea in his kitchen and he was sitting in a chair, with a blanket around him. He'd gone all cold, you see... like he'd come back from the Arctic. Poor man! What? Well, I did get help. All I could think of was Paddy at the hut. He always knows what to do. He was in the Korean War you know... a medic I think. Anyway, he came and took care of Harry with me.

Joan, it was awful! Poor man. I wish I knew more about first aid. Dangerous? Well yes I suppose it was. He did have a gun. I never thought of the danger. No, I haven't told the police. Paddy took the gun away.

I'm sure it'll be fine, now. Paddy's going to tell the doctor. There'll be some help tomorrow. Locking my doors? Why should I? Oh, I see. Well yes, I'll lock my doors. Promise... goodnight, Joan, goodnight, love. Don't worry about me. I'll be right

Dinner with a Poet

Julie, Julie, it's me... listen. It was fab! I think this mystique... it's working!

He's lovely. We went for a meal in this sort of basement restaurant in Leeds. You go down some steps... it's all candle-lit and there's jazz playing. Oh, he's such good company! You know, we talked and talked... we both love the Brontës. We both love the Romantic poets... and guess what? His favourite place is that mountain in the Lakes... Blencathra. Wait for it... he had a poem about it... he read the poem as we were eating dessert! I asked him to read it... yes, he just happened to have it with him. What? No he's not a pseud! No... he's a genuine poet. I was so impressed. Well, he read it sort of quietly. We were at a corner table... no, it doesn't matter! Stop teasing, you little pest!

You're jealous because I've got myself a proper boyfriend at last. Yes, he is a proper boyfriend! I really like him, Julie. You can talk! Remember that weirdo you had who took you to the dog races and then left you when his mates turned up?

So anyway, I had avocado... then a sort of unusual fish dish... and orange sorbet. He's asked me out again, and you know what... oh yeah, we kissed alright! As we walked for the bus, he took hold of my hand. It was great... I didn't want to pull my hand away at all! He kissed me on the cheek as we waited for my bus... and then he went for it, and kissed me on the lips. It was lovely!

Tall? He's about an inch taller than me. Yes, I have worked that out. You do, don't you? Well, maybe you don't but normal girls do! *Oh, you are a nuisance... but I like you!* Like that comedian says on telly.

There's just one thing. He does go on about being different. He says we should break free of everything. He talked about that march last week, you know, the homosexuals... they marched in London. Do you know any people like that? Samantha at school was gay, wasn't she? They use that word, *gay*. Yes, I know. My dad says that not long back, it used to be illegal to be gay. How cruel is that? It's just love, and love is the answer to everything. Andy says he has friends who were in the march. He talks about how rotten the law is and how small-minded people are who say rotten things about anyone who doesn't conform.

You know what? I think I'm in love with his mind as well as his body. That sound stupid? Okay, so I am stupid. You always said that. We'll have a giggle, anyway.

Julie, Julie, listen. You know I was never a romantic, right? Well he's changed all that. I think that people... the right people... *make* you romantic. They do, I swear. He's lovely. Can you believe that in a dump like this, in darkest Yorkshire where a tap on the shoulder is a show of affection, there's a young man like Andy? I mean, how did he come to be like this? I have to meet his family. I go all soft when I think of him. Is it the real thing, Julie? Is there such a thing as *the real thing*? I think about him all the time – is that the test of whether it's real or not?

Ring me tomorrow. I'll tell you more... 'Bye.

Hooky Tries Again

I did, yes. I did ask her again. I said I would. Edita is such a sweet girl. I really don't want anyone else. Now listen to this. I chose my moment. I had the ring. Very expensive it was. I had to borrow some dosh from my father. Now, I took her to see a film - a romantic film. Then I had a dinner booked at a place where they charge you to stand on their front mat. Okay, I'm stretching things a little, but it is top drawer, let me tell you. They have a Wine Adviser who comes to the table and goes through the options for you.

In the film, I held her hand. She looked at me, all soft like. Then she bit my earlobe at one point. When it went really dark she let her hands wander and it was just wonderful... but you don't want to know that do you? The thing is, as we reached dessert, I took the ring from my pocket and sort of stealthily held it ready for when she came back from the loo. I produced it just as she sat down again and... well, guess what happened. Right. She laughed. Then she said never in a thousand years. *' I like a man in my bed but not in my life, '* she said. *'I will not be number four, '* she said.

Mates, you're looking at a poor sad Hooky. No wifey for him. You know, when I was a kid at school my Roman nose got me my nickname, and it's been a kind of bad luck thing ever since. I think if I had another name I could find a wife... or maybe another nose. It's an unlucky nose maybe.

Okay Paddy, I'm back to work. I've seen the clock.

Three Months

Please, please, my old mates, would you sit down at this table, now please. Get your teas and your toast and please, I beg you, listen to me. I'm going to say something now that will rock your minds out of this little hut and into the no-man's-land of human life at its most ruddy basic.

I went to the quack this morning, before coming in to do my day's graft. It was just like every other visit to Dr Gotolski. He's always been most understanding to me. The very greatest emigrant medical mind what escaped Hitler's mad plans for his Jewish race. That man has the sharpest brain of any medico east of the Rockies, as my dad used to say. He always comes up with something... yes, yes, he did tell me I needed sex. That was one of his more groundbreaking bits of advice. But anyway there I was this morning, with a particular pain. Right here... in my groin. Then there was another one - a spasm - across my chest. So Dr Gotolski gave me a thorough inspection. He poked in every hole and tapped in every little tender patch of flesh. I thought I was going to pass out when he did the rectal thing.

Anyway, he finished, and then he sat me down, like you are sitting down now, and he tapped his pen on his desk. Then he flicked through a very thick and heavy book, scratched his ear, then frowned. The brilliant Dr Gotolski, refugee from the Nazis, brilliant man with a sad face and a serious attitude, pulled no punches.

I have three months. He spoke the words slowly. *'You have three months to live, my friend.'* That's it. I have three months. He explained in technical words what was wrong. My condition is incurable. Awful words to hear, mates. Awful. But I took it like a man. Mother will be absolutely destroyed. You are looking at a man with three months left on this earth... it's gone very quiet. I'm so sorry to have upset you all. But there it is. There is no hope. I asked for a second opinion. He said that was not necessary. All my measurements added up to three months...if I am fortunate. You know what he said then? He said to me, *'I should begin to make your final arrangements.'* Final arrangements. Has anybody got anything to say?

'You better find that woman, Gordon.'

Thank you Simon. I knew I could rely on you to say something stupid! You talk about women at a time like this? I mean, there are other matters. Who's going to have my stamp collection? I have six twopenny-blues and a full collection of the Gold Coast since 1910. Then there's the car: my Austin. To say nothing of Mother, and who will care for her.

Three months. So drink your tea and think on that. The man what you look at now, he's doomed. I can feel my pulse weakening even as I speak. Three months. No need to look so glum about it. I'm so sorry, I put a blanket of gloom into the hut, lads... I should never have said a word. You've had to be very understanding with me, I know that. It seems a strange thing to say but I've been expecting this. Oh yes, I've felt all my sinews weakening, my blood supply sapping away; it's been coming. I've been held together by drugs and elastoplast. But you know what? Being with you lads, my special mates... it's been the best life a working man can have...

I just worry about what's going to happen to Mam.

The Search Goes On

I'm Patrick Lanagan. I look after the site. May I help you? Simon, you wanted?

What did you say your name was? Dinchop? Well Simon isn't here just now but... oh here's Mrs Baker. She's been looking for Simon as well. He's a popular chap! I'm Paddy by the way... I'm a sort of leading hand here. I look after the hut. What do you want to see Simon about, Mr Dinchop? Oh really! Oh dear. You're very angry. Mrs Baker has been a bit angry as well, haven't you? Well the last I heard, Simon was checking all the door locks and garages on Asphodel Crescent. He should be back before five. It's a grand fine day and we're putting in a full shift. He's been putting in a full shift on your wife, Mr Dinchop? Whatever do you mean... oh, I see!

Can I make you a cuppa, both of you? A cuppa usually calms things down a bit. Please don't slam your fist on my table, Mr Dinchop... it's only plywood. Very fragile. Only takes the weight of lunchtime mugs and plates...

Mrs Baker... do sit down. I can see you're with child! Oh, it's Simon's child? Are you sure? Mr Dinchop, come back... no, no violence please. Well I hope you find him but let's be like grown-ups shall we?

Please, Dot

Please Dot, take it easy will you? I'll be home as soon as I can... it'll be just after seven. Yes I know the dockers are out. They're talking about a state of emergency! Well I've got that here in the Asphodels but that's not in the papers! Look, we're nearly there. I reckon by August tenth. Yes... a few weeks now. So you just think about that beach, that sunshine, the flow of wine, nothing to do but relax... think of all that! Yes I know life's not easy just now. The dog... yes, limping. Well it's not a cancer. The vet said that. Rest easy there, my love. I know I owe you. I owe you. It's all been empty promises in the past, yes I admit that. But this is a big job. A major job. There's that bonus you know. Yes... August tenth and I still get the bonus. I've negotiated with them. No, they won't go back on their word. We've done years of work for them... just ease off a bit. Why don't you go for a game of bingo before I get back? Right... go with Joyce then. You get on well with her. She's a good friend, chuck. See you at seven.

Just take it easy, Dot, please. Strikes? Oh yes, there are strikes coming. No, it will not affect us. Not the building trade, love. Two weeks? Yes I know. Maybe the middle of August... we should finish around the middle of August. I know I keep giving you more dates. But as soon as I know for sure, I'll book that holiday. I promise. Yes. I promise. It's going to be really worth it, you'll see. The Asphodels will be a great place to live.

Dear Nigel,

I thought it wise to respond to your last letter, and to explain the situation with Mr Patrick Lanagan, the man, you will recall, who manages our yard and hut. I feel I must apologise for giving the man perhaps too much support and understanding. The fact is that we are dealing with a true unfortunate. Mr Lanagan has lost his home and his property here in Britain. He has a brother and family over the sea in Ireland, but nothing and nobody here.

I am writing, consequently, to ask a favour. I know that this is highly irregular, but I would like to ask if Mr Lanagan could occupy the hut merely until we end the work here at the Asphodels in around ten days? I feel that this would not create any problems for anyone around the place. As to the horse, that has been returned to a local stables, from which the poor beast had wandered and drifted into the land around our yard.

If you could allow this, for such a short time, you would be saving an old man from life on the streets and perhaps from serious illness and deprivation. In the building trade, as you know, sometimes we have to carry folk, make special allowances if you see what I mean. I ask you to see things from my angle.

Yours hopefully,

Barney Rathbone

Popped the Question

I was rebuffed, Paddy. Rebuffed. Rejected. I asked Katy to marry me. I said we were a duo with a future. Guess what she said? She's had an offer from a top agent and they want her for TV. Yes, TV. No, not me. Just her. Seems there was a talent scout in Otley and he spotted her. *Spotted in Otley* I said, trying to lighten the atmosphere. I said it in my daft Uncle Albert voice. But she must have seen that I was weeping inside, under the brave face.

How can I carry on, Paddy? I'm wrecked. She's going to be on telly and where will I be? Al Hinchcliff will be doing Uncle Albert at the West Bopley Conservative Club... to an audience of ten.

I do love her, Paddy. What can I do?

Centre 223, Fair Lawns,

Nairobi

Kenya

Well son, you will not expect this as you sit there under the African sun! I persuaded Dad to let me send this letter along with his. He's given you all the local news and told you all about his obsessions and preoccupations. He ought to have an outside hobby, I told him that. He spends too long staring out at the garden and worrying about other people's lives when his own needs looking at.

I'm writing to say that you're not to worry about me. I have my books, my radio and some embroidery when I can manage it. I've made two samplers since you went to the Dark Continent. As you know, I'm very self sufficient. But one thing I do miss is our long and silly chats about all that comedy stuff you like. I know you love The Goons and you can do all the voices, but your dad hates any kind of media really. He could read history books all day and never be bored. He's not good on small talk either.

Time goes so quickly. When I first fell ill, it dragged of course. But I found so many things to occupy my hands, and my mind. I can listen to music all day of course. Sometimes I put The Lark Ascending *on the record player and just let my mind float away onto the moors, imagining that lark. You know, when your father and I were going out, he once took me up to the moors by*

240

the Brontë parsonage. We walked along towards that little waterfall. But before you reach that there's a high bank, with long grass, very dense. Well, on that lovely day, as we walked, up above us there were larks, deep in those tufts and depressions along the bank top. Oh, it was heavenly. I can see it now, hear it now. Do you have larks in Africa?

Remember- you are not to worry about me. When you do come home, we'll go out and have a meal and plenty of wine, and you can regale us with tales of Africa. As you know, I always wanted to travel, though my favourite place was always India. One day I'll get there.

How are you for tee-shirts and socks? I'll send some anyway. Tell us anything you need - anything at all.

Love and hugs

Mum.

The Footy Match

Now then lads... settle down. It's raining again. Mine's a pint of bitter. No rush for you to get back to work, right? You've come at a very opportune moment, as I'm putting together the story of that footy match... you know, the one in the trenches on Christmas Day. Of course it's true... I was there. I played centre forward. It was snowing. There were bodies shovelled to one side as we cleared the pitch and made a touchline out of urine. Eddie the Drink pissed the lines out. His piss was always bright white as he had the clap, but it made a grand touchline.

Then the Bosch team appeared and we all shook hands. Kaiser Bill was in goal for them... he was! Yes, he was! He kept his *Pickelhaube* on and he swore worse than any fishwife. Oh yes. The referee was our sergeant and the linesmen were orderlies that the Major brought in. Well the wind blew and the snow came down but we passed the ball around. It was heavy as a brick and the lace used to lash your eyes and forehead. Well we slugged on, and it was all very scrappy... no score at half-time. Do you know, we shared cake and biscuits and drank ale... one of our lads... a teacher back home... told a joke in German and they all laughed their socks off. Kaiser Bill slapped his sides and laughed so much he started coughing.

Well, off we went again and the lads were crowding the touchline now, shouting and joking. Then, with ten minutes left, their centre half clattered me so hard in the box that I went down in agony. The ref blew for a penalty. Can you imagine that? Can you imagine how I felt? I was to take the penalty kick, as I was the goal-getter you see... well I was facing Kaiser Bill. There he was, wearing a thick woollen jumper and his lederhosen, jumping up and down like a springbok, and the Bosch soldiers all threw fruit at me and called me Tommy Thick-Head. The kick would probably win the game. My heart was in my mouth, lads. But you know what? I watched his eyes. He was watching my eyes, looking for a clue as to which way I might kick it, left or right. I could see that his eyes followed my eyes to the left... my left. So I kicked the ball to my right! Well, he looked so pathetically sad hurling himself against the post as I sent the ball to the other corner. The ref blew for a goal and pointed to the centre line and the Kaiser was knocked out! I saw that his *Pickelhaube* was bashed down over his brow and I tugged it off him. He said thanks and you know what... he promised to make me a nobleman! He did... *'Tommy, I shall make you Prince of Flanders when we win zis damned war!'*

So you see, if only we had lost that bloody war, I could have been royalty. We won the game one-nil of course. Nutty Backhouse nodded off the line with a minute to go, and we all lifted him high, singing *God Save the Queen* for the rest of the day...

I wouldn't say no to a bag of crisps, actually. Still raining is it?

Brenda and Paddy

Morning Mr Lanagan. I'm sorry to bother you again, but you said if I needed help... good. Well you see I was told you were a medical man, and well, the blob... I mean my little girl... I'm not sure everything is okay. Yes, yes I know I should have seen the doctor or the midwife. Yes. I know, but you're so close and, well, I don't think there's any movement down there. Mr Lanagan... is she... is she *dead*? Where is Simon anyway? I need the dad here. My husband, he's still away on the roads... I *know* that Simon is the father. I know it, Mr Lanagan. You will have a look? Oh thank God. You're a wonder! I'm going to kiss you on the forehead. I'm not bothering him you see. I'll never tell Phil... I've just come because I think that Sime should know. It's the right thing to do.

Yes, I'll lift my blouse up, of course. Well, if anybody comes I'll tell them you're a medical bloke, like they say you was in the war. What? Can you hear anything? Oh, your face is cold as ice... why do you live in this horrible old hut? Moving? She's moving? Oh that's great. I love you, Mr Lanagan! Cocoa? Yes, please, cocoa.

Is it true you were a medical soldier? Oh, in the Middle East. I see. I suppose you saw dead bodies and that. I see, yes I know that soldiers never want to talk about what they've seen. I think you're wonderful, Mr Lanagan. Here come your boys. Oh hello Mr Gordon... is Simon out there? What? He's gone home? Been sacked? Oh no... I need him. Mr Lanagan, is that true? He's been sacked? Well, if you can tell him I need him please. Yes. He's the father. I can't tell my husband, he'll go bonkers.

Thanks for the cocoa Mr Lanagan. You can be her unofficial granddad.

There's nothing wrong? Thank God for that. If you felt her kicking then that's fine. Sorry to trouble you. Yes, I know I should see a professional... I promise that I will. Yes, I'll book an appointment with a doctor. Promise, yes. Promise. You *were* a medical soldier. I thought somebody said that. You worked with an ambulance? What a life you've led, Mr Lanagan... the cocoa is delicious. You could tell me about it if you like... being in the army. My dad was in the army but he never said a word about it.

If you don't want to, well... men don't want to talk, do they? Not like us girls. We can't shut up! Thanks for the drink anyway, and the help with the blob. I'd better be off now, Mr Lanagan.

Go Home

For the love of Christ, Gordon, go home! There you are, up a ladder, yanking the pipes about, and you a dying man! You should be filling every day with joy, my friend... I'm a good Christian, most of the time, and it's my duty to help my fellow humans see sense. The doctor has told you... I mean you've had the words spoken, the words every man fears and dreads to hear... and here you are, working as usual. Have you spoken to Barney about money? About time off? What about your ma? Who is caring for her?

Listen to your friend, Paddy, and get off home. Tablets? How many are you taking? By the Seven Holy Men of Ringsend! Fifteen tablets.... every day? You'll be high... it's not natural. Come down, get your coat, and go live! Don't you feel ill? Are you a robot or something? Every day now is precious, Gordon. Will you come down and let me have a chat over a cuppa with you? You need to listen. I'm not a saint but I am a religious man, and it pains me to see a man so close to meeting his Maker carrying on as if there's nothing wrong... what? You feel perfectly well! You probably do, but what on earth is going on in that body of yours is anybody's guess! Sometimes I think it's a miracle that you are still walking around amongst us.

Good, now you're sitting down. Good sense at last. Now shouldn't you be at home? Why spend what little time you have left, working like a Trojan at the site? Barney's bringing in two new blokes tomorrow anyway. Good. You stay there. Now promise me that when you've drunk that cuppa, you'll get yourself home. Good. Let's have some sense around here.

It's time somebody listened to me. I'm here to take care of you lot. It goes with the job of giving you shelter and a cuppa when it's all too much.

I'm sure there's no pain, but for the sake of Holy Christ, you're bound for the next world, man. You should be taking care of your affairs. Yes, you've said you own nothing... and that you owe nothing. That's grand. But what about your family and that? What? All alone? No missus? No kin? Well yes, we are sort of your kin, I see that. Oh Gordon, please, please go home and prepare... prepare... yes, to pass on. To pass on to where the Lord will take care of your soul.

Live it up, man, while you can. You have no faith, I see that. But life is for *now* in spite of what Heaven might be, man.

An Agent Appears

I'm not kidding you, Paddy, there's a chance I'll be on telly! I was at the Binkley Tivoli on Saturday night... that is... the Maori Maleroa was, like. I was just being crushed by the Pudsey Poleaxer... he's a giant of blubber, that one... and this face appears by the ropes and he says, *'Ever thought of having an agent, son?'* Now, after the fight, I was feeling a bit sore, like, but he comes up and he says do I want a pint? So we were soon the snug of The Royal Guardsman and he says he could get me a television contract. It was like a dream come true, Paddy... only one thing. He wanted me to change my ring-name. He suggested Bonebreaker Briggs, the Binkley Bruiser. Over the top? Do you think it is, Paddy? Yes, I thought it doesn't have the *style* of the Maori Maleroa. It hasn't got the *class*. But he'll get me on telly... I said yes. He takes a cut, like, but he has contacts. He wants me to put on more muscle, and eat more pies. Do you think I did the right thing? Well it's a bit late now, as I signed a form he had with him. Small print? Why?

He wanted me to have new gear, new trunks, a different face-mask, all that sort of thing. The big break has come, lads... the drinks are on me!

Come Down Here!

We know you're up there in that toilet. I want to speak to you about Denise. You know what I've come about... we're not children. Come down and talk about it like a man! I am Jeff Dinchop. You probably know that surname don't you? I'm here on behalf of my brother. He is Denise's husband. Now you need to understand that I'm a police officer and I abide by the law. I'm not some mindless thug. If I wallop you, there will be no visible marks to be seen. Mrs Baker's husband is not as understanding as I am... he's a lorry driver and he's well over six feet... and that's just round the waist. Now he's in Germany just now, but he'll be coming after you, and he's not as gentle as me. For God's sake come down out of that loo.

What do you mean, you can't? You're locked in? Oh my giddy aunt, what sort of a man are we dealing with? Look, I'll come back tomorrow. You'd better be in that hut, or I'm sending some of my lads for you. Mrs Dinchop is not well enough to come out just now. Can you hear me? Look, it all started as gossip. Then I heard that my brother was all for battering you. As an officer of the law, I can't let that happen. I've told him he's in danger of committing an assault... I want you both to discuss things, like men, like grown-ups.

Bloody well COME DOWN HERE!!

Dizzy

Oh Paddy, I'm going to faint! I feel all light-headed... I'll just sit down. Yes, I know I shouldn't be here... I'm a dying man. Yes, I should be at home with Mother. There's nobody else... nobody else... if I'm going to kick the bucket I might as well do it while I'm at a place I love, Paddy. I'll just sit here. Yes, building work is all I've ever done. I'm only happy with a shovel or a trowel. If I leave this world with a spirit level in my hand I shall die a happy man... tea yes, strong tea... no, no ambulance please! It's only a dizzy spell. It's my pulmonary whatsit... knocks all the strength out of me. I can't lift Mother into bed any more... I have to shout for the neighbour... terrible thing, life, isn't it Paddy?

Yes, I know you said I should stay at home. But... but it's so lonely. I don't want to die alone, Paddy! Just let me sit in the corner and have a bit of company. I could keel over right here. I think it's spreading, the thing, the virus. What a terrible word that is, Paddy – virus. I mean the little bastard gets into your bloodstream and it shatters all your system. The little bugger is in there now, breaking down my tissues. I'm food for worms, Paddy, food for worms!

Yes, okay. I'll get a grip. I'll take control. Aspirins, yes, give me two aspirins. You're a good man, Paddy. I want to leave you all my stamp collection, and my autograph book. I've got Charlie Chaplin in there. Yes, I said I had nothing in the world but I do have these little treasures and they are for you, Paddy Lanagan, because you're a bit of a saint. You're the only saintly

250

bloke I ever met, though one of my quacks comes a close second. Remember, when the will is sorted out and I'm six feet under, the autograph book is yours. I've got Roy Orbison in there as well...

We'll Write

Julie – he's off away... the building work is all done! But he came to the Club and he said, *'Look, Cynthia, I promise... I will write to you. I've written my address on this bit of paper. Take it, please.'* He looked me in the eyes, all sincere. Oh he was so sweet. I had to say, yes, we would write. Do you think we will? Well, it's up to me, I know. But I do like him. Is he special? What does special mean? If you believe the stupid magazines, a woman is supposed to feel a twizzle in her innards! A *twizzle...* oh I don't know! It's a word my mum uses... she's dafter than I am. You see, the thing is, he's very intense. I'm not sure I'm ready for *intense*.

The Day of Destiny Approaches

Now lads... see what it says on the calendar? August seventh. Now, in two days you know what is going to happen? I've asked you all here, in Paddy's wonderful hut, with mugs of tea and special chocolate biscuits supplied, to remind you all what will happen. As you will all know - apart from young Andrew here - immediately after the clock strikes nine o'clock at Knotworth Town Hall two massive, swanky Bentleys will pull up outside this hut. Then four men will alight, and direct their steps to me. I will be standing ready for them, with a smile on my face and a feeling of complete confidence that my crack team of home-builders have made the Asphodel project a model for the construction trade to wonder at.

Now, the gentleman leading this little group of men in smart suits is a certain Mr Bentham-Caldwell. He is a former officer of the Engineers and he is perfectly normal apart from one little character trait. He thinks he is God.

Now, Sime, how do we cope with a man who thinks he is God? Bow down to him. Yes, good man, Sime, good man. Now I understand that you are not now being pursued by irate husbands or pregnant ladies? That right? Good.

The inspector wears a stupid bowler hat and he's bald as a coot underneath. His moustache is somewhere between that of Hitler and a Mexican bandit. He's a pain in the posterior, but he's good at his job. Be patient with him.

253

Mr Bentham-Caldwell will inspect every nail, every screw, every toilet flush, every garage door, every doorstep, and so on. He and his minions will tick boxes on their clipboards. By eleven o'clock they will meet with me here. I want you all out of the way by then. I want you waiting outside in a straight line ready to bow to him when he comes out and proclaims the Asphodels to be completed.

This brings me to the jobs still on the list, and I want these all done by six tonight. I will inspect them. Then tomorrow, even if it rains all day, the job will be complete and ready for His Nibs. Here is the list: the drive and number seventeen; the guttering on the last house on the Avenue; the gate on number thirteen up this road - swinging loose on its hinges; the grate outside number ten on the Crescent- wonky. Finally, the walls from number eight to number twelve on the Crescent - last layer of engineering bricks to go on. Understood?

The main thing is that I'm proud of you. The weather has been on our side, yes, of course. But what matters is that you all got stuck in, grafted, did the jobs on the daily lists, and we find ourselves on schedule. I'm proud of you all. It's not been easy - especially with that leak at number fifteen.

One other thing. I've told Mr Dinchop that you, Sime, will not be working here again. He thinks that you have been sacked. We have a solution – you will wear your big overcoat and Al's cowboy hat... yes I know it's sweltering... you'll have to do it.

Mr Harold Mond,

No. 1 Asphodel Ave.,

Knotworth,

Yorks

Dear Harold,

It's a while since we heard from you, and I'm getting worried. You said that the lovely lady was taking care of you. That's wonderful news. We were so worried when she wrote to us. Are you more than friends now? I've read about old widowers going into themselves – I mean, cutting out everyone and not being sociable. I hope you haven't been like that. We'll have to come across. It's just that we've had a bereavement, as my neighbour passed away. Evelyn she was called. You didn't know her very well. Also I've taken up a part-time job. Yes, at my age. But I do like it... working in a shop for a few hours. It's ordinary, but it's all filling up life, as usual.

Please drop us a line, or ring, even. It's been a long silence.

Sylvia

Very Sorry But....

Mornin' everybody. Nice day. Look, will you sit down and drink your tea... if you could finish that toast, Simon, good. Barney, I have something important to say, and I want to thank you for being so patient and understanding, like, but the fact is, I'm not going to die after all! No. False alarm! Turns out the tests were wrong. The old ticker is going to tick on a bit longer. So I'm very sorry but I think I'm going to be alive after the houses are finished, after all.

There we are. I've said it. I don't mind telling you, I was nervous about giving you the news.

Well, don't all rush to congratulate me will you? I thought you might think it was a big deal. My mother did. She said, *'Thank God, I've got my boy back...'* that's what she said. You know, I thought something strange was happening when I was dizzy all Saturday night and I started talking to myself... it was like somebody was talking inside me... you know the feeling... what? What, Barney? Well my ticker was not beating right. When Dr Gotolski did his tests he was not feeling well. You know, I thought at the time that his hands were shaking. Turns out he has a drink problem. He's a genius though... still a genius.

It's funny... it's like I've come back from the dead. All this time I've been thinking about myself being in a coffin... being lowered into the earth... then being floating around in the post-death condition like… yes, I thought of myself face to face with my Maker, Paddy. Yes, I did.

What? Why are you upset, Al? Oh the collection. Well, you'll all have every penny back. We haven't had the holiday mind you. Though Mother did spend some of it on the bingo. But you'll all get your money back, I swear. Don't be upset, Sime... I've got some put by in the Post Office. No, no, never did I set out to diddle you out of any money. Never!

I don't care what you think of me. I know I've been a menace... but the fact is, I'm not going to pop my clogs, not yet anyway.

Any toast left?

Clearing Out

Cynthia, pour us a coffee, will you? I have to tell you about this afternoon...

We were all gathered together to lay the concrete on the drive at number 10. There were myself, Gordon, Barney, Paddy and Sime, and Sime was wearing a very long coat and a hat that came down to cover his face. This was because the Dinchop house was just across the way, opposite, and there had been what the cowboys call a ruckus for the previous hour. Mr Dinchop was at a bedroom window, and he was hurtling objects down, onto the lawn. Behind him, Denise Dinchop was screaming.

Sime took a position at the dark side of the lorry as the concrete was tipped out of the back. We all shovelled and spread, and a gang of part-timers came to help, brought in by Barney for some casual hours' pay. There were enough bodies for Sime to hide behind. Small items had been thrown at first. The lawn was strewn with boxes, cardboard and wood; there were items of clothing and shoes; then there were bedroom things such as a mirror and some glass ornaments.

'No, stop, stop! You're crazy!' Mrs Dinchop shouted.

'This is next... the bloody radio you keep up here... do you have that on while he screws you, eh?'

'Please, stop... please stop!'

We couldn't stop. The concrete had to be down really sharpish of course, while it was liquid. But Sime kept peeping around the tail of the truck, squinting to watch.

Mr Dinchop was standing there, holding a radio in one hand and pushing his wife back with the other. She said that her mother gave her that radio. But it was no use. It was destined to be chucked down, cracking into pieces as it hit the stone bird-bath. Then we heard no more of Mrs Dinchop, as more and more things came sailing through the air. *'You want the man? You can have him, Denise. I don't care. Last week I wanted to break his jaw. Now I don't care. You're not worth it. You know what you are? You're a slag. A slag! Yes, I can see you lot over there, is he there, the lothario? Is he there... the wife-stealer? Well you can keep her mate. She's damaged goods.'*

The neighbours were trailing out now, and staring. An older man walked to the lawn, looked up, and said, *'Now this will never do, old mate. Let's cut it out, right?'*

'Dr Stone... just mind your own business!' Mr Dinchop said this with a savage tone in his voice, and then he threw another batch of shoe boxes out of the window.

'Mr Dinchop, this is Irene from the corner shop.' She was in the gaggle of people now. *'This is Irene... give over will you? That's enough. The poor woman is distraught.'*

We finished the concrete and we sloped off to hide away in the hut and drink tea. But the shouting went on for another hour. Then I came here. Honestly, if that's marriage then it's not for me... what? Oh no, I mean, that can't be marriage, can it? I mean they're not really in love are they, not if they do that!

What you say? You don't want to be Cynthia? Thea? You want me to call you Thea? Okay then. Yes, it is more bohemian.

New Name

That sandwich should win an award! Tell the lady at the shop Andy. Tell her what the secret recipe might be. It might look like an ordinary sandwich, two bits of bread with a slice of Red Leicester and a tomato between them, but I'll tell you what - it's *cordon bleu*, mates, *cordon bleu*. But guess what - your old mate Hooky is not Hooky now! No, I went out down the pub in Leeds... a new one with a weird design. Anyway, I met this woman. Let me say that Edita is firmly in the past. I've moved on, lads. The new woman is Felicity and she's Scottish Italian. Her family make ice cream in Glasgow. Well, it was love at first sight. We looked across the saloon bar and we both smiled... No I don't want the bun, Sime. You have it. Are you listening? Good. Well we talked and talked. That is, I listened and listened. Well actually, that was the one teeny-weeny problem. I couldn't really understand her words... not all of them. I have difficulties with a Scottish accent. I fixed my stare on her lips. I think she thought I was handicapped or something. But anyway, we kissed goodnight and she's going out with me again on Saturday and she's lovely, and I think she's number four!

Okay Paddy... I know, back to work. Yes, the young lad came to help. He's casual I guess? Right. He's a good lad. Quick he is. Anyway, that's Felicity. She's the one. I think that love has been looking for me and she's found me. It's the real thing this time, mate. I can feel it here, inside. I can. I might need some help in lip-reading because her voice is strange, but that's not enough to stop true love, is it?

I see the mistakes I've always made. I've been too soft-hearted. Yes, true. Soft so that I get exploited you see. But she's not got a bad thought in her mind, Paddy. She's like a goddess, I tell you.

Mrs Ivy Carver,

No. 1 Asphodel Avenue,

Knotworth.

Dear Sis,

You've been playing nurse, I know that. You have mollycoddled him and fed him up. I can even see that you've been at work to settle his mind. The poor man has had what they call a breakdown I think. But he's come through, and now, if he's so much in danger of becoming distant again, I have a few suggestions. You might think it's all rubbish, but a sister has to try!

Remember the rhubarb? I feel sure that if you do what we girls are supposed to do – the way to a man's heart is through his stomach – then the man will give in to gentle pressure and start to look for the romantic bones he has somewhere in him. All men have them, believe me. They need us to help them to find the damned things, but they are there.

The next weapon in the arsenal is flattery. Tell him he looks good in whatever he's wearing. I know that's hard if he's an overalls and stained shirt sort of bloke, but you can always switch to 'Aren't you clever, dealing with that sprocket or spigot or something!'

My first boyfriend had the same problem as your neighbour. He seemed to freeze when there was too much

263

femininity in his orbit. They do that – blokes. In a gaggle they find their voice, but it's a boring one. It's somewhere between apes and buffalos. So find a time when he's fixing his bike or his car and then turn on the flannel. Don't overdo it of course. Keep it gentle and steady, so he's not aware that you're laying it on.

In fact, if you combine flattery and the care of the belly then how can they resist? That's where the answer lies: flatter his ability to put away Yorkshire pud! There we go. Ask him to Sunday dinner, make a foot-high stack of Yorkshires and off you go, lay it on... my word, you can eat a square meal... by heck you have a manly capacity for good food!

Notice that word, manly. They love that word, Sis. If you tell a five-foot pipsqueak he's manly, he'll buy you a slap-up meal with wine and even some conversation above a leer and a grunt.

I'm going on, but I can't bear to see you all bereft, on your own. You make me bring to mind that old song Oh no, Antonio... left me on my own-io... *we used to sing that didn't we?*

Anyway, give me a ring and let me know the latest.

Going Loco

Joan, hello? That you? I got your letter. But I had to ring you because there's been progress made! By heaven there has. I had no need to ask him to Sunday dinner... not at all! He came out of his shell... now, I called to him over the fence, as he was messing around with his hanging basket, and guess what? We got talking, and after a few minutes, he invited me for a day out... we went trainspotting! It was lovely. He took me to a railway station, a sweet little old place. There was a gang of blokes all wrapped up in long coats and carrying flasks of tea, and we joined in. Harry had sandwiches and cake for us, and a big flask with enough tea for both... and Joan, it was very strange! These men, they hang around, chatting away, all about locos and their names and numbers... one man went on about a rare one he'd spotted somewhere in Norfolk the week before. They all fired questions at him. You know the strangest thing? Harry never stopped talking... and not *once* did he mention nuclear war! Now wait for it... wait for it... in one of the lulls between trains, Harry put an arm around me, and he asked if I was enjoying myself? I gave him my best natural smile and said yes. I meant it, as well. Now we ladies, we're professionals at doing the false, dishonest smile, aren't we? Well this was the real thing. Never have I enjoyed a cuppa so much, just gawping at a tender and listening to Harry describe the work done by the man who shovels the coal into the furnace thing. You see, I know what a tender is now! It's a coal-car that carries the fuel. There you are. Your sister is now a trainspotter.

I'll ring again, keep you updated. He talked about a trip to Weybourne, wherever that is. Hard to believe, I know, but I have a picture of a loco pinned up in the kitchen. It's the A Class *Mallard*. I'd give my best necklace for the chance to shovel coal in her!

Absent Friend

I thought Arthur was on the counter today, Mrs Kent? What? His mother phoned... what happened? No! Attacked? What for? He doesn't get into fights, surely. Oh, I see. Well send him all our good wishes, and we hope he gets better soon. Usual for Paddy and Gordon. Here's a list for the casuals. We've got four labourers here for the week. Irish. Paddy knows them. Yes, there are some animals around. There are some folks that nothing will change, nothing will shake them out of their pits of despicable behaviour! The human being, Mrs Kent, is capable of evil... in fact it's not fair to the animals to use that word about us... I've seen some people who are lower than the worst scum on earth... we'll send a card. I'll tell everyone in the hut. Mrs Kent.. I have to tell you that at college, my best friend is gay. Yes, he's the best friend I ever had. Doesn't Arthur have a... a special friend? I'm sure he mentioned him. Yes, I see. I thought so. They were both hurt? It gets worse. Give me ten minutes with the scum and I'd teach them a lesson, for sure!

Yes, the casual blokes all seem to want beef dripping. Myself, I'm going off meat.

See you tomorrow, Mrs Kent.

Inspection - Morning

Right, everything is ready for you, Mr Bentham-Caldwell. Yes, tea first I suppose? It is a lovely day in Yorkshire. You put that very well, sir. Welcome to your little team as well. Patrick here will make the tea, and I think we can offer toast as well if you're peckish. Good. Do sit down, everyone. We have plenty of chairs in here... you probably saw the rustic armchairs outside as well... oh, a gift from a local resident. This is the very best tea available here, sir. Oh, you would like to speak to the men? I'll call them in. They're all outside.

Now come in lads... Mr Bentham-Caldwell would like to say a few words.

'Good morning, noble sappers. I have met most of you before. I recognise most... not that young squaddy though... Andrew? Pleased to meet you, Andrew. What a marvellous job has been done here... now, you know the drill. My junior officers and I will conduct a thorough inspection of every domicile you have created by the sweat of your labours. At eleven hundred hours we shall meet again and you will face a full report. There will be no excuses for shoddy workmanship and if I find any evidence of such, I shall not deem the development to be complete. Consequently, no bonuses will be awarded. I know how much you relish the thought of a hundred crisp pound notes slotted into your wallets... but we shall see... we shall see... now off we go. I know that I can rely on you good workers, the best we have in the firm, I know that. See you later.'

The Syndicate

Jim, I have to tell you first that I've been allowed to stay here. The boss has given permission for me to stay until the work finishes. You know there was that bother over me looking after the place? I was only cheering it up. Just adding a little colour. But the bay was the last straw. I had to walk along the lanes up the Bradford road and ask at all the doors about who might have lost it. Damn it, there was an owner... a bloke who ran a stables for kids learning to ride. I've had to take down the bloody lean-to as well.

Anyway, now to good news. I've gone and done it! I've put my last hundred quid on *Gastronome* for the big handicap at Sandown in a fortnight. That's all I have. It's a last throw of the dice. But if I win on him, I have big plans. It's all about the States. I'd like you to join in. I know you have dosh saved up.

What I'll do, dear brother mine, I'll start one of them syndicates. You know the game. You advertise in the racing paper saying you have a yearling that sprints like greased shit and ask two hundred smackers from each member. Then you have, say, a hundred members, all paying two hundred and with my arithmetic you have twenty thousand quid. I know what you're thinking. I need the baby horse. Well you must know that the animal charities have nags to spare. They can't feed them all and they give them away. What do you think? Of course it's possible! Who's going to check out the little beggar? You get a wee foal, barely out of the staggering and wobbly stage, take a photo and then make up a pedigree. The trick is in the names, like *by Shooting Star out of Quickstep to*

269

be called Starstepper. See? No, I'm not talking rubbish. There are rules and regulations, yes. I'm not entirely barking mad. I know more than a little about the turf. I've been haunting the bookies since I was fifteen, haven't I? You cannot deny that.

Of course it's not illegal. Look, you know as much about the racing game as an Arab knows about icebergs! All I'm asking is that you make me a fancy letter, appealing for the subscribers. I'll be the boss of the syndicate.

Fraud? No, it's not fraud! There will actually be a nag involved. I'll stable it in the shed, out of the way so the boss can't see it. I'll put him in the lean-to with Golden Girl. I'll have a whole string if this carries on! Jim, I'm not flannelling you... I've speaking straight. You know I always talk right with you. It's the gospel truth!

No, it's not fraud! Shit, he's hung up. He's put the phone down on his own flesh and blood!

Finishing Touches

My good building friends... you brickies, plasterers, carpenters and labourers... I've adored telling the episodes of my life to you on these wet days in Yorkshire... I've loved it. But you know, even the great epic stories come to their last act, and the Murgatroyd memoirs reached the final curtain last night. I hope you don't mind if I read out my concluding paragraph... oh a pint of bitter, please, young man. Here we go:

Gentle reader, you have followed the ups and downs of the life of this old sweat with admirable patience, and I hope that my adventures in bedrooms and on battlefields have conveyed the requisite joys and terrors of this life. It is all one huge, baffling adventure, and now, as I have little time left on this earth, I leave you with the most poignant moment of my military life. This was when I said farewell to my comrades after the 1918 Big Push just before the Bosch threw in the towel. The fight had raged on through the night, in a storm that would have rattled the Jungfrau; death stalked the ranks and screams cut the foul air. By the morning, I was the only man standing. I gathered my last ounces of strength and set about digging graves. At three in the afternoon, I stood to attention and saluted the long line of mounds beneath which lay my comrades. Then, something rubbed against my puttees. It was Alfie, the faithful Jack Russell who had been my comrade through the worst hours of the conflict. He barked, and I could swear he said, 'Enough.' Well, dear reader, you have had enough of me.

Oh, thank you, gentlemen, thank you. I don't deserve such applause, but this old scrapper salutes you!

Hello son, it's your dad. I simply rang to ask where the devil you are? My letters have been going to Africa but there's been nothing from you. Mum's very worried. If you get this message, please, son, ring me back... let us know that you're well. It's such a frightening world, what with all the trouble in Ireland... and the national state of emergency! So, let us hear or read your words, very soon.

Last Night's Show

Paddy, she was on TV last night. Katy. Did you see her? She had three minutes on the Dotty Doller show... you know, the cross-dressing comic? She was funny, Paddy... so bloody damned funny... my Katy. She should be *my* Katy. It should have been both of us up there on that stage. Both of us I tell you... I could weep, Paddy... sorry, yes I'll pull myself together.

Shiner

Hello Andy. Yes, I'm back... and I know it looks awful. A real shiner. I was aching all over yesterday. Philistines, they were. Neville and me were at the pictures. We went to see *The Lion in Winter*... you know, the one about Henry II. Neville's into all that medieval history. Oh yes, he even dresses up and goes to historical parties. He dressed up as Louis XI once and had a full beard, tights, golden doublet... the lot. Then this bloke told him that King Louis never had a beard! You have to laugh! Yes, I'm laughing because if I stopped to think about what happened, I'd weep all day. We were at the pictures, near the back... as you do. Neville put his hand on top of mine, you know, as I rested my arm by the side of the seat. Well, these morons behind must have seen him do it. First it was whisperings. You can imagine the language they used. But you know what? It was an encounter with the cavemen, and nothing will ever wipe them out from the streets. You have to face up to them. I've a shiner, so what? It'll go. I'm tougher than they are... cowards. They are no more that meat-heads. But I'll be something better and higher than they will ever be. This world, my friend, this world is a fallen world. My dad used to say that. For a long time I had no idea what he meant. Now I know.

Usual meat pie for Barney? Thought so.

Inspection – Afternoon

Now you men, stand at ease. Nothing to worry about. I've had my platoon of assistants look over every little wall, floor and roof of the place. I have to say you have done a splendid job, and I heartily recommend that the Asphodels are completed satisfactorily! The only tiny thing I'm asking you to do before we sign the papers is tidy up the edges of that paving at number ten... can you see to that, Mr Rathbone? Good. Well, I suggest you retire to somewhere providing a glass of something stronger than Adam's ale, and Mr Rathbone and I will join you after our little confab in the hut... and by the way, I have to congratulate you on this fine wooden hut, so well maintained... and a pleasure to behold.

The bonus payments will be sent to Mr Rathbone of course. Never have bonus payments been so well earned. I think that some cups of strong tea all round would be in order... with perhaps a dash of something stronger, Mr Rathbone? Hard graft deserves a fitting reward. I've been so impressed by your application to work. I know the deadline shifted once or twice, but look, it's still the summer. Let's call it a late summer deadline, and you met it, right?

Then, of course, we move across the way to the new estate... the Boxwoods. I take it you're all keen to sign up for that? Yes, Paddy, the hut will have to go. It is sad, of course. But there we are. Unless of course you're carrying on working for us... on the Boxwoods? I was told you were heading on to pastures new, across the mighty ocean? Well, have a think...

Deltics

Joan, you okay love? No, nothing to worry about. The opposite actually. I'm ringing to tell you about the day out yesterday. Joan – do you know about Deltics? Didn't think you did. These are Class 55 diesels, built ten years ago. High speed they are. They are named after the Napier Deltic power units. Oh yes, I had a full lecture from Harry. But you know what? I love it... the trainspotting lark. Oh, now I can see what all the fuss is about. There were about twenty of us, hanging around Doncaster station. We saw some... one was a loco that Harry had not seen before... on its way to Scotland.

Joan, he's a different man with a notebook in his hand and a bunch of enthusiasts going on about HST's and stuff. You know what as well? They're not all men! I met this interesting woman called Sheila, and she is mad on Deltics. She had this lovely memory of being in class at school, just a few years back, and hearing the sound of a loco called *St Paddy*. She said that the Deltics all had names – not only the boring numbers. Sheila said that at lunchtime, she and some mates would scramble down a field and take a spot where they could see the tracks, eating their sandwiches and waiting for the next engine. She was so happy... there was joy in her eyes when she spoke... the same joy you can see in Harry's.

It's so good to have some kind of understanding of him – I mean, he's not an easy man. Well, you know. I don't need to go on.

Keep writing, Joan. I like to be updated. I'll put a postcard with a Deltic on it in the post for you, love. The age of steam! I tell you, there was never anything like it for sheer beauty. The age of steam, Joan! Just think on that, chuck.

You're Not to Worry

Hello Sylvia... yes, it's me. Sorry I haven't rung for a while. I got a bit down. Had to go to the doctor for some tablets. He suggested I talk to somebody. Well I mean I'm talking all the time aren't I? I'm talking to you now! But anyway he said he meant a different kind of talking. In fact he said that I would talk myself better. Them was his words. Talk myself better. But Ivy next door, she's been wonderful. If I want to talk, I call on her. Do you know, I think she actually does like locomotives! I can't get her into philately or coins... but well, it's unusual for women to like trainspotting, so I'll be happy with that. You're not to worry, Sis. No, I'm not lonely. I'm never lonely. I like my own company... oh, yes, I like Ivy's company as well, of course. You know, I always found it hard to talk to people... you know that anyway. Well she's easy to talk to. I can fill a whole day with sticking stamps in my albums or looking through my train records, but yes, I can see that folk need other folk.

Ivy says she'll help me clear that room. You recall that I have a room where I tend to put by stored boxes of collectable stuff? Yes, well it's got out of hand I suppose. Ivy says why don't we set aside a weekend and put it all in order. Yes, as long as she doesn't throw anything out... I'll not let her throw anything out, Sis. Will you come and make sure that she doesn't do that? Please? I know I can tell her, yes, but that might offend. I'm not sure what words to say to her. She's been kind. Sis... Sis, this Ivy... she *held* me. That's what I'm saying. She held me. I was down, down as low as can be. She came and she *held* me. I didn't tell you that. I was hearing the air assault. I was

279

hearing the fighter planes as well, then the big ones, shaking the ground everywhere. The house rattled, Sis. It rattled. Then this Ivy, she came. I thought she was a ghost. I thought a ghost was holding me. I thought it was our Mam.

Dearest Renee,

If you have nothing better to do this evening after you finish at four, then I'd absolutely love to see you. Spend time with you. Just us, I mean. There are hours of light left, so you can do nothing better than meet me at the gate by the back of the Club just after four. Bring food and some beer. If you say no, I'll weep.

Love, Paddy.

From Africa

It's from him... let me read it to you. I can see you're in pain, my dear. This is what he says.

Dear Mum, your letter was wonderful - a real tonic. First, as to larks, yes, we have lots. The red-capped lark is the one I see most. I'm not really a naturalist but when you asked, I did some research and asked around. The important thing is that they do give you delight in their song, just as you said about that day in Haworth. Sorry this is such a quick note, but I wanted to let you know that I'm fine, and I'm busy as usual. More and more teaching as the days pass. You two take care. I'll be home soon.

Isn't that wonderful my dear? He's a good son. He's the best.

The Question Popped Again

I asked her. I asked Felicity. She thinks I'm called Norman... what do you mean it's a stupid name, Sime? It's a normal name. Norman the normal. He's the normal man. I said will you marry me, and I held out the ring. Yes, it's the same ring as before. Yes I know that's wrong. I don't care. I love her. Anyway I asked her and she said *'Yes Norman,'* but then she said a lot of other things and I don't know what it all meant. Norman is better than Hooky, surely? But hell, Paddy, what's a man to do? I mean when she stopped talking she asked me a question and I have no idea what the question was. I'm not rude. I'm not prejudiced. I just can't translate what she says into Yorkshire! What happened? Well she slammed the ring on the table and ran off.

Gather Round

Now a little bird tells me that your work is all completed, lads, and that the Asphodels are to be left to the people who will love and cherish them! Well that's splendid. Mine's a pint by the way. This will be our last little session together, looking back on the good old days when men were men and women fled for the attic and locked themselves in for safety!

Another little story? Well I suppose I could dredge out one more from the cobwebbed room of the past. I'll tell you about the damned Boers and about a real hero. Oh, powerful chaps with rifles they were! Could pick off a gnat's bollocks at two hundred yards! Well one time there was I, with Corporal Socks Bainbridge... a Geordie lad, awful hygiene problems but a heart of gold. We were there, trapped on a ledge on the side of some ruddy *kopje*, bullets whizzing past. Six men in our detail had had holes shot in their ears and had put their cufflinks through for decoration... a number of men had crooked limbs after too speedy operations under the surgeon's knife... and we had no idea what to do. Then old Weevil Knoblock, a veteran of the Zulu business, scrambled out of the dusk and he said we should cause a landslide. The Boers were a hundred yards below us he said, and if we prised loose some large boulders, and rolled them down, we could cause mayhem and then run like hell as the dust rose. *'You lot run around the kopje and I'll cover you by shooting at any Boer who stands up... off you go!'*

We did. I have never known such a brave man as Weevil Knoblock. It was the most noble sacrifice I knew in my forty years of soldiering. The rocks went over the ledge. There was screaming. Men called out for their mothers as they were crushed. A few stood up and were gunned down by Weevil. But as we reached the safety of the dip at the east of the *kopje,* I looked back, and there was Weevil, all ammunition gone, screaming out Her Majesty's name... *'For the Glory of our Queen Victoria!'* He was cut down by a dozen bayonets. Brave man... brave man.

A Good Woman...

A good woman is hard to find. That's what they say, right, Paddy? I've given up trying to find the perfect wife. I'm going to wait until she finds me. Hooky Scrope, the man you see before you, mate, was not meant for marriage. No, I'm a single man, by nature. You know, it's all in the genes. Destiny. I've searched the world for the perfect woman and you know, she just is not there... what? Well, do you have to accept what there is? You think they're all second-best? Oh, except your own. Oh I see the joke. I guess I have to lighten up. Is that why they don't want me, Paddy? I'm too serious? My father always said I needed some smile-creases on my face. He said that women could tell if your creases were from smiles or from worry. Mine are from worry aren't they, Paddy? Worriers don't get the perfect wife, do they? Be straight with me, mate.

No, I know they are not mass-produced in factories. They're not dolls. I know that. It would just be nice if the right one came along and took me by the scruff of the neck and said, *'Be mine, you lovely man!'*

Thanks for listening, Paddy. You're a true friend.

Forearm Smash

You lie there and look all seductive and that. I'll show you one of the moves. Well, you did ask. Now this is a forearm smash, see? This ironing board will have to do for the other wrestler. Imagine he's coming at you, looking all fierce, right? Now you can see from his expression that... no, Denise, nobody gets hurt. It's all pretend. Yes, I know it sounds as though there's flesh on flesh, but it's all done by trickery. We all have to learn how to grunt and fall, and whine in pain and that... now, the ironing board... he's coming at you so you lift your arm like this... you step forward, putting one leg forward, like, then you push your arm up and into the man's face... like so!

No, no. It doesn't actually hit him. You'll just have to come and see me... see the Maori Maleroa in action. I have to prepare, Denise. I don't have a drop to drink all morning. I go for a run at seven. Then I work in the gym. By twelve I'm practising my *haka*... all very professional.

I wish you were my wife, Denise. I'd treat you better than your old man. He's never here. Look at you, lying there like Cleopatra. You know, in that film. Liz Taylor. You could get a man excited, Denise, with them eyes and them bosoms. No, the ironing board will not do... I need you.... now!

Success at Last

Jim, Jim... is that you? Are you sitting down? Oh by the seven Holy Men of Ringsend... it bloody won! Bloody *Gastronome*... it bloody won at a hundred to six. What? A hundred to six. Well that's around, well nearly seventeen to one. I won nearly two thousand quid! Are you coming to the States with me, dear brother? Look, it doesn't end there... Renee put fifty quid on as well! By God, we're almost rich. I'd say well off... we're well off. Of course, of course... I won't gamble it all away. Trust you to throw shit on the rose garden! Yes, I know that shit is good for the rose garden... oh please, please, spare me the lecture. Just be happy for me... for us. Renee and me... with cash, with plans!

The little beauty was held up at the back, on a tight rein, moving real smooth, and then it was brought round the outside at just the perfect time to go past the front rank... oh sweet it was, coming up close by the rail, won by a length. The jockey is a genius! Oh, he's called Murr, Lenny Murr I think. Not Irish.

Shall we buy a horse, Jim? What do you think?

Fine, fine. I'll ring again later. You have to get to Mass, of course. Talk again soon.

Arthur and Neville

Put your hand on my hand, Neville, and sod the world. Oh I adore this one... Brahms is so powerful and then so sad. He sends you through the whole range of emotions... I know you love him. This wine is very welcome too. What is it next? Oh, Debussy. Yes he's great too. You know, it's strange when you think about it... what we're doing here. I mean, two hundred people all staring at four musicians on a little stage, completely silent, each one with their own thoughts. My thoughts dart everywhere. I think of streams, lakes, waterfalls, then mountain peaks... when I listen to that Brahms. I think of thunder and then mighty massive sunrise yellow... and the beginning of the world... Brahms does all that to me. What do you think of, Nev? Me? You think of me?

Put your hand on my hand, Neville, and sod the world. You know what? You, me and a classical concert... and the thought of a glass of wine later, of course. Couldn't that be good enough for paradise? I think so.

We are never again going to be troubled by the porridge-heads who jeer and taunt us. No, never again. There are those among us in this world who hate to see anyone happy. They don't understand love, Nev. They are afraid of it. They're told that footballers don't cry and that being a man is being something with the sensitivity of a brick. Life is about grinning and bearing it all, not there for joy and celebration.

There, I've said my piece now. Thus endeth the lecture. Put your hand on my hand and stuff the lot of 'em out there if they can't leave people to love where they choose and how they choose.

Packing Up

Hello, Jim? No, I'm not talking about the bloody syndicate. I've given up on that. You were right, as usual. You always were the clever-clogs of the family, always bloody right! But no, I'm ringing with news. The job is done...

Jim, I'm just giving you a call to let you know that the work on the housing estate is all done. The lads have packed up their tools and thrown them in the boots of their cars. One by one they've all pulled out, with the usual handshakes and vows to meet again for the next job. Young Andy has gone off to college. He's into poetry and such. Did a good job though. Now, I have to tell you, the boss told me to knock the hut down and get it loaded on the lorry. Sime is helping yes... very heavy sides... yes, but wait a minute. No, I'm not packing it up. No. See, I was finishing my tea this morning, standing outside by the flowerbeds, and I heard this birdsong just behind me, at the end of the long side... well, yes, I walked to look, and up in the junction of the guttering... well there's this nest. I saw the darting flight of a little brown hen-bird, its beak stuffed with stringy worms. She dropped on that corner guttering and satisfied the cluster of demanding wee mouths that depend on her. *'The hut will have to stay,'* I said to Barney. No, I'm not packing up. There's been too much of that.

Renee? Oh I think I'm in love with her, Jim. My knees go shaky when I get all close up and such... oh, yes, and I can't sleep at all. But what can I offer her? Let me confess. I've rung to let you know that... well, sadly, the money... yes, I lost it. Everything I won on *Gastronome* I lost in ten minutes in the bookie's on Boxwood Lane. I was born a fool. Yes, it went on a nag, a damned bow-legged donkey. Oh hell, what shall I do? I've not told Renee. I'm skint, Jim. All I have is a hut on a street corner, and even that is illegal.

Yes, you are right, though. I do have flowers, and a little family to care for. And I'll tell you this... she makes the best cheese scones this side of the Rockies! The hut will have to stay. She has a little house... one up and one down, outside toilet... that kind of thing. Like they had in 1900 you know. Yorkshire has not moved on. She has no heating but a coal fire... but I could marry her, like.

I said I was going to take Renee to America. Yes, I had enough to maybe buy into a stables or work for a trainer out there. But that's gone the way of all flesh... thank God for... what? You're not well? In what way? Nothing serious, surely? The ticker? You mean what? Heart failure? Jesus Christ, brother mine, you mean your heart fails? Doesn't a person exit this world when his heart fails? Oh, like it doesn't work at full throttle? I see. Six lots of medication? You're kidding?

Anyway, I know I've not got long left on the site, but there is a possibility of a new one... and you know what? I'm going to make a hut that will be the mother and father of all site huts. Oh yes, I'll have a flowery carpet, and some of those wooden shelves that slot into each other and so you need no nails to set them up... then pictures. I scrounged some landscapes from a man who was clearing out his garage... and I'll make the garden at the back where the boss's spies can never see them. Yes. Well, not a bed, but I know where there's an old but workable sofa, just left outside for the scrap-man. I'll be having that little beauty.

I know I've been told not to, but there's always a way round problems. Like the lean-to for instance. I'll make one on a moveable frame, so that it bends into a flat shape when you want to sort of hide it. No, no, there will be no bother. It's all hot air from the company. Truth is they like a man on the site night and day. It means they don't have to pay for any security. Yes, of course. I've thought it all through.

It's a special place, a hut like this. You understand. It's in our Irish soul, brother. Something fundamental. Something appealing to the travelling man. The rootless man. But all the pressure to put a stop to it, well that's made me adapt. I've had to be inventive, creative. Again, an Irish trait I think. Haven't we got all those wonderful storytellers? We like to be rootless, but we long for a sort of halfway house. That's my hut. It's halfway to being a house.

Yes, at the moment it's a hut on a street corner, but a man can have plans. Now ring me next week and I'll have something for you for the Sandown meeting. Right. You take care of yourself. 'Bye Jim.

The Smythe-Caldwell group

Yorkshire Forward estates

Dear Mr Lanagan,

First of all, may I simply say how pleased I am that the situation concerning the hut was resolved. You responded to my complaints with common sense and alacrity. In particular, you returned the horse to its rightful owners. I thank you for all that. We did not want any kind of bad press for the company, did we?

I am writing to let you know that your application to be site foreman for the new Boxwood Estate project has been successful. The work will begin on 1st September this year. We would like you to set up the base facilities before then, when the labour force arrives after recruitment. Your first duties will be to secure a yard for materials and establish the pre-fab building which will be delivered in the last week of August. I feel sure that you know exactly what needs to be done in preparation for our next stage of work.

I must remind you, however, that in your next duty as yard and hut manager, there is to be no repeat of the unofficial decorating and animal husbandry which you attempted to develop at the Asphodels. The site is purely and exclusively for building materials, lunch-breaks and planning sessions regarding jobs in hand. I have to insist that you scale down the domestic dimensions of your established pattern of work with us. If nothing else, there *is a tremendous sense of wastage - of time I mean. Time spent growing plants could be given over to plastering for instance.*

Your work for us on the Asphodel site was impressive, and your superior, Barney Rathbone, recommended you for this position.

Very good wishes,

Edward Bentham-Caldwell.

The Picnic

Well you are a man of surprises, Paddy Lanagan! You have swept me off my feet! The last thing I expected was a horseback ride and a picnic. You're a man of surprises all right. You know, here we are, a mile from Knotforth, with nothing but hills and farmland... apart from Gawpham pit over there... a few miles off... and I love it. I could get used to being swept off for food and beer! You're a lovely man... you know, as I have some beer in me and my tummy is comfortably full, and the world is looking good, I can tell you that, as a widow who has known love and lost a man she treasured, this is the first time since he was taken away that I have felt comfortable with... well, with any man, really. You're easy to talk to, Paddy. Yes, the last bun has been gobbled and there are only nuts left... oh and chocolate! What, no food... what's that then, the little packet there? Who cares about the States anyway? Look at this land around us...

Oh Paddy, are you serious? It's a beautiful ring... yes, yes, I will. I'll take you, horse and all. I know that all you have to offer is a horse and a hut. But what more do we need? I have my room... my little flat over the shop. There's just enough room for us there. Just one thing... please call me Irene. Meanwhile, kiss me, kiss me like we were twenty again.

Paddy Lanagan, you're the best kind of romantic – you bring food, not flowers. I'd rather have a bag of chips than roses any time, love.

Murgatroyd in the Spotlight

There he is, Thea, on a little stage, where he always wanted to be... Mr Murgatroyd! Will he never run out of stories! I know you find him too coarse. The humour, it's an acquired taste. Not for women, I know.

Yes, I *did* call you Thea. I remembered. I made a special effort to listen to you, do something that pleased you, and all that. No, I haven't been reading women's magazines. You want to be Thea... you hate, let's just say the other name... and so Thea you are. Look at him, he's like Yorkshire's Winston Churchill, sitting up there, brandy on a little table next to him. I think he's actually going to be introduced, like a guest star. Maybe he is a star. Which tale will kit be do you think? The football match along the trenches? The condoms? He really is an awful bloke! How old is he anyway - two hundred? Well I'm told he was born in 1897, so he's only seventy five. It's just that he *looks* very aged. Can I kiss you, Thea? I mean, nobody's going to throw us out for indecency are they? This is 1972. I like kissing you. In fact, though you might not be surprised, you're the first girl I kissed. Sorry, woman... the first woman I ever kissed. Oh you knew, did you? Is it that obvious? Right. Course. Well I'm really glad that I'm learning on you. No, don't tickle me... no, I put that badly. I didn't mean to say *on you*. I meant with you! There are things I'd like to do *on you*, but not here. No, stop, don't tickle me there...

Oh my God, Gordon has just come in. The man has no shame. First he was supposed to die, then he was told he would live, and then he caught rabies, or so he said. He looks fine to me.

Denise and Sime

Get in, Denise... get in the car. We're off to the Club. Then you're going to stay with me for a while. That savage you live with... yes, used to live with... you've seen the last of him. Get in, throw your bags in the back. Right, in you get. That's better. It's you and me from now on. You're better off away from that bully. Not only is he a bully, he's a boring oud cod as well. I've seen faces like his on the slabs at the fishmarket.

Plant a kiss on my cheek... right there. Yes, lovely. You and me... you've been staying *where?* Irene's flat? Oh, above the shop, I see. What about your stuff... what happened to it all? Anyway, you need that divorce... all in good time, yes. All in good time. First thing, I'm going to look after you. There's a room at Mam's. Yes, didn't I tell you, I live with my mother? No, no, I'm not a mother's boy. Far from it. Look at Nigel the Nutcracker, he lives with his mother, and he's tough as a brick wall. Nobody teases him about being a mother's boy... if they did they'd lose all their teeth!

There... now off we go. A drink or two at the Club and then home with me. I'm going to take good care of you, Denise. There are pints and wine waiting for us at the Club... I promised the lads I'd be there.

No, don't cry, Denise. Yes, I'm pulling up. We're going nowhere until you're feeling right. There... the engine's off. Put your head on my shoulder... now you just sleep if you need to. I love you, Denise Dinchop.

A Word in Your Ear

Barney, can I buy you a drink? Oh, you have one. Right, well can I sit here a minute. Sorry Mrs Rathbone, I won't keep him long. I know we're celebrating the work being done and that. Barney, you know how I was signed up to work on the Boxwoods? Well I was fine when I said yes but....no, not the click. No, the cancer has not come back... no, actually, the thing is, I found the... I'm going to whisper this... *the comfort woman.* Yes, it was very good, yes, but you see, I sort of... I'm whispering again, as your missus is very near... *I caught a... what they call a sexually transmitted disease.* I'll be fine. I'm still keen to work but I'll need some time.... yes, I'll go, Barney, I'll go. Enough said. Yes, I know this is not the time or the place to... yes, I'll go now.

Young Love

Thea, Thea... I want to kiss you. I know we're in public. I don't care. This is the new age... I'm never going to be a semi-detached damned Asphodel dweller. I want you to come with me... when we're not students any more... and walk all around the globe, sleeping under the stars. What do you think? Have a think about it while I kiss you. I've been practising... kissing the mirror. Don't laugh! Okay, laugh then. I love your laugh.

Oh that was the best ever... I mean....there were no others. I mean it's the best ever... with you. Why are you laughing? Ah, the toilet. Yes, hardly what a great poet does, is it? Would you kiss.... one more time... such a pathetic failure? Oh, oh, Thea... keep your hand there... keep it there, and don't stop whispering... I love your voice as well. You can talk rubbish all day and I'll not care. I *dream* about hearing your voice...

Of course I'm rubbish at this. They don't teach you about rumpy-pumpy at school. The biology lesson involved cutting open a cow's eye. That was your lot. We all thought the reproductive system was something to do with farming. Philip Prentice was the kid we thought most mature. He gave us some tutorials about sex. Oh yes, he said that ladies had zips down their bellies and that's where babies came from. I made you laugh! Great. That was the point of all my drivel you see. This feature in a mag – it said *laugh them into bed.* Well it worked. Now you're laughing again. Good stuff.

Yes, I will kiss you again. Yes, no, don't stop...
don't stop...

Ménage à Trois

Now, Sime, I can see that you're very happy here with this lady... no I'm not here to cause trouble. I heard from a conversation in the shop that there was a celebration do on here. Sime, I felt that you should just know that this bump, this is Shirley, your daughter. Oh, hello, missus, so he's moved on to you then? Very fond of the fair sex, is our Simon. Yes, I'm sure you are very surprised. You had no idea did you... oh, you did? There was talk about me, was there? Now, I'm not here to ask for cash or anything. I certainly don't want YOU. No, I simply wanted everyone here to see what a slimeball you are, and that you are going to be a father... oh there's no doubt. My Phil was away for quite some time when we had our... our fling. Is that the right word? I think so. Your life is a long, messy succession of flings, isn't it, Simon? Well, I've said my piece... enjoy your time with him, missus. It won't last long. You do know he's the Maori Maleroa? Of course you do. He goes on and on about it. He ought to go to New Zealand and daub himself with paint. Oh yes, a real New Zealand athlete from Bradford. Sime, your blob – Shirley in here – she will never be part of your life. I wouldn't want her to be exposed to such a waste of space! What Yorkshire lass would want to admit that her dad was the wrestler on the telly who did that daft dance? Sorry, ladies and gentlemen, for interrupting your fun. I'm off now, and I won't be hanging around Knotforth again. Oh, are you not going to do a *haka*, then, Sime? He usually does a *haka* in the bedroom before jumping onto the bed. You've got that to look forward to, Denise. 'Bye.

Stranger

Dad... hello, Dad? I'm in Manchester. No, Manchester. Not Africa. I'm home Dad. I'll be with you in a few hours. Yes, it's not a joke. No, I don't have to go back. I need some thinking time, that's the point. Yes, we've a lot to catch up on. Are you alright, Dad? Are you crying? Give over... you'll start me off. No, I've eaten. I had a big meal in the airport. Great to hear your voice too. See you very soon, Dad.... very soon.

Just one thing. I've got somebody with me. It's been a secret, but I know you'll be happy when I tell you. He's called Esperance - Rance for short. Yes, *hope*. It means hope, course. What? He's been a little lost kid, Dad. But now he's with me. He's two. I adopted him. He came into the village on the back of an old lorry. You're a granddad now! Mam is a grandma! Course she is. Silly thing to say… can she come to the phone? I can tell her about him.

The Final Tale

Welcome to the Asphodel Club. I've regaled you with stories from my long life. I've got to know you all as if you were my family. I know you've been across there, building homes for our families. Noble work, gentlemen, noble work!

Well, as we're here to mark the occasion on which the houses are all done, I'm going to tell a tale about love, ladies and gents. We all have a first love, right? I've witnessed the real thing here in this very room... hey, young Andrew? There is nothing in the world more beautiful and exciting than the love feeling when you know it's true, when it's genuine. Course for me it were Françoise Dequin. Her eyes were blue like a summer sky and her voice was t'music of 'eaven. We were *marrer to bonny*. That's a Yorkshire phrase meaning, two folk, one soul. Closer than sardines in a tin, like.

There's never been no reason to talk French. I learned it in t'War. Some on us knew more French that *Inky Pinky Parlez-Vous* tha knaws! But I learned enough to say her name proper. Excuse me while I wipe me eyes. I'll start at the start.

It were like some gert church, I thought, arches, curves, moulded roofs... and it held gert steam-breathin' metal monsters. There were smells of oil and soot, something clung to me breath and I took it into me lungs like soup. Mrs Topwith stood beside me as the train pulled into t'long platform and we both stared ahead, expectin' a herd of folk rushin' from the guns that had shattered the

305

peace of their own land. But no, gradually, folk stepped down onto t'strange floor and stood in lines of two and three, each luggin' a case and a bag. I held out my school slate what said *Bienvenue nos amis Belges*.

I had bars of chocolate in me pockets and I took some, ready to give out. Mrs Topwith said she'd choose some and I was to give 'em chocolate.

Before I realised, Mrs Topwith had gathered four people together and she was talking French to 'em, and she tapped my arm and said, *'Chocolate, Murgatroyd.'* But before I could move a muscle, there she was, standing right in front of me, her face invitin' me to step into a dream.

Well we all got took to a big car, like, wi' a chauffeur. It were t'Mayor's car. Tha climbed up and sat on these seats... like slabs of marble they were... and I sat there and 'utched up to this bonny lass. I'd carried her suitcase on for her, but when I took hod of her bag, she tugged it back and frowned. I moved away a bit. Then we were driven to a posh part of Leeds - up Headingley somewhere. Everybody got out and Mrs Topwith told me to carry some cases in while she spoke to this toff in a dark suit. That's how it all started. They were all Belgians and this lass... well, I got her name from Mrs Topwith's list. Françoise Dequin. I asked Mrs Topwith about her, and all she said was that the girl played t'violin. I knew then what were in that case

I couldn't stop thinking abaht her. Couldn't sleep... me one thought in me mind was of her... I saw her face all t'time like. Then I heard abaht a concert that she was playin' in and I went. I sat down in this big hall wi' all these posh folk in suits. They were all dead serious, but all I could do were smile... as I stared at her lovely face and thought that angels lived i' Belgium.

I were too scared to talk to her that night... but then I went time and again to that house i' Headingley just hoping she might come out. I sat one night, shiverin' so much me teeth chattered, praying Françoise would come out for a walk or summat.

A day or two later, I met her on t'doorstep while deliverin' some groceries from Mrs Topwith. She came out, smiled at me, and I felt my face flush red. I asked her if she needed owt and told her me name. *'Murgatroyd, lovely name.'* She said it French tha knaws, like *al-bare.* I thought, next time I'll asked her out, and I did. I took her to see a brass band i' Roundhay Park, but her mate came wi' us. It were quite an ordeal at first, but then we all laughed and her mate left us alone for a while. We walked round t'lake and I took hold of her hand. Just for a second, I could feel her pull her hand away, but then she laughed and squeezed my hand. All we did were talk about her home... and her music.

Well, a week after that I were a soldier. I remembered we drilled in town and there were a big crowd watching us. When we stood at ease by t'Town Hall, I could hear t'sound of violins.'

There was a concert inside the hall. I knew she were playin' in there. She told me. She'd been invited to

307

play wi' a professional band. I imagined her there, her head to one side, her cheek against that glossy wood... never saw her again. I were in France afore tha could say Jack Robinson.

My pint was refilled as Ken, the landlord, hummed a little tune he'd heard from a show at the Empire. Norrie, my old mate, spoke a few lines from a poem, *'By day or night in weal or woe/That heart, no longer free/Must bear the love it cannot show/And silent ache for thee.'* He said it was by Lord Byron.

Then old Batty Feather couldn't bear the quiet any longer and said, *'I see there's injuries for t'game at Huddersfield!'*

The Smythe-Caldwell group,

Yorkshire Forward Estates

Dear Mr Lanagan,

You may recall that in my last letter I made a reference to the hut. Your hut is the one I refer to. I have been willing to give you a certain leeway in this matter, but unfortunately the time has come to demand that the rather domestic additions to that workplace now be removed, if you wish to continue working with us in the next stage of our Yorkshire projects

This has not been initiated by myself, but from my superiors, as someone locally has informed them of the situation regarding a bay mare which was housed at the hut. I had no knowledge of this animal, and therefore I suspect that the presence of the beast was hidden from me by yourself and your confederates.

I must ask you to remove all gardens, decorations and animals which might be evident at your hut. I would appreciate your swift conclusion to this matter, and then we may continue, with yourself as the materials manager and site security at the next location.

Yours sincerely,

Nigel Smythe-Caldwell

Gay Pride

Nev, you and me, we're going to walk at the parade next week, march through Knotforth with heads held high, and in my head there's going to be a film reel running... I'll see myself in 1970, with so few others like us, sworn at and abused... and I'll feel that new sense of being valued, as my fellow workers value me... yes, and you know what, Nev? I'm going to kiss you. Yes, in public. If we get arrested then so be it. Yes, if I get a black eye, like I said I did back then, well, I read somewhere that you put a leech on it. That takes the blackness away. Shall we take a leech on the march? No, I'm joking, Nev. I'm being trivial. I've determined to be more trivial in life.

What shall we write on the banner? Okay, *Love is the answer*. Yes, we could have that. Yes, love *is* the answer, of course. Well, *Gay and proud in Yorkshire* would be more provocative. Good – let's be damned well provocative, Nev. What? Oh, even better! Yes, we'll just have *Arty and Nev*. I like that.

Sorted Out

Mr Lightfoot, Mr Lightfoot... what are we going to do about you? I don't know how many times you have sat there in my office, looking at me for some kind of wonder cure, and for God only knows what malady. Mr Lightfoot, I would hazard a guess that your poor body has suffered every illness in the handbook. In fact I suspect that you *own* a copy of a medical handbook, is that right? Now, please, destroy that book. Would you do that for me, please?

The first thing I'll do is spell it out to you in plain English. *There is nothing at all wrong with you. You are a well man.* There you go. Now go and do some wholesome activities. Gardening for instance. Put your effort into meaningful work. All will be well. There is no reason why you should not live a long and happy life. All the signs are good.

No, no, I assure you. This is the truth. I have administered every conceivable test. Your bones, your muscles, your skin, your organs... everything... these are all healthy. I have to say that you need to lose a little weight. Perhaps cut back on the beer but... now, Mr Lightfoot, don't be upset about it. This is good news. There now, let's not have any tears. You are a well man. You are fine.

Here's a handkerchief. Now, I have no prescription for you. There are no drugs necessary. Let your mind rest. If you really want help to let your mind go easier, I can book you some time with a colleague, a specialist in matters of the mind...

Yes. Now that's brightened your mood I see. No, you will not be put in a straitjacket. No, there will be no asylum. Mr Lightfoot, he will simply talk to you, ask you questions. It's a therapy. Yes, I see you look a lot better. I'll arrange a meeting. You will be hearing from me soon.

Goodbye, Mr Lightfoot. Try smiling, being happy. That's the ticket.

The Big Thanks

I've called in again to talk to you, Big Man. I wanted to thank you for the rain. You sent enough of the stuff to make sure that the lady and myself had some time alone. You know what? I think I fell in love. Yes, the rambling wrestler has finally found The One. Technically she's married, but we'll soon sort that out. It's a loveless marriage.

Now there is something else. The thing is that I like being in here, talking to you. I'm hoping you will really listen of course. But then, talking to yourself can be satisfying on its own. There's many a lonely wife said that to me – that they talk to themselves. Well my wife will never say that. A woman wants to feel wanted and to feel special. No more of that flitting about between ladies. No. I'm smitten with Cupid's arrow.

I thought I'd call in. I like this quiet spot. The thoughts are easier to find. Words come along more honestly, I find. But you would know all that, of course, being God.

Coach Tour

Ladies and gentlemen, honoured guests of Yorkshire Forward estates, welcome to our tour of the newly completed Asphodel suburb. From where we are now slowly crawling our way towards the edge of the main Huddersfield road, it is only a few miles to our destination. You will be served tea or coffee and Yorkshire parkin, in your very comfortable seats, by our two young ladies from the hospitality suite at our HQ in Leeds. The coach will progress in a slow and stately way towards the Asphodels, and our approach will be from the rural side, well away from the arterial roads. Now, I understand that some of you were in the guest party before the Asphodels were completed. You people will see an astonishing difference!

To everyone else I say prepare to be utterly enchanted by a sight of what the future of British housing could be. Well, I am Nigel Bentham-Caldwell, and you will immediately recognise that name from the headed letter-paper on your invitations. Yes – our board is responsible for the ultra-modern family homes you are about to see. Of course, I wish to entice you to invest in our next ventures, one of which is adjacent to the Asphodels... oooh, sorry for that lurch. Just a dip, hey Phil? This is Yorkshire after all – hardly flat!

Here comes your refreshment service. Lesley and Donna have only recently come to join our staff at the firm's HQ. You will notice our little silver rose on their chests... we like to think that we represent a new, glittering county, a place totally different from that place of cloth caps, pints of ale and greyhounds you see in the cartons, eh girls?

This is merely a taste of proper Yorkshire entertainment and the welcome you get from folks up here. Oh yes, community... it's all about community. We don't just build bricks and mortar and roofs... no, we build a community when we set to work, ladies and gentlemen.

Drink up, and eat up, and then as we round the next bend, you will see the beginnings of the new suburb, with the Priory Hotel on the left, spanking new and I notice with more than a sprinkling of brand new vehicles parked around it... now here we go, soon to be in Knotforth. Yes, here we go. Now, see the very spacious driveways of the first house on the right. Now, that's the Montana, as in your brochure.

Oh now along here, there will be a rather charming little detail... a hut or *materials base* as I should call it... yes, a flower garden. Oh well yes we encourage a certain element of creativity in our foremen you see. Oh, a horse? Well there is a horse, but it must be merely visiting... oh yes, the man and woman are embracing, I see. I have no idea who they are. Oh they're waving at me. How strange. Yes, they do look jubilantly happy.

Phil, take a left will you, miss out the old club. Good, Now, any more questions? There is more parkin. It's home-made of course. No, no, the couple do *not* live in the hut. Well, I suppose they are merely the lovers of Asphodel Way.

Lightning Source UK Ltd.
Milton Keynes UK
UKHW020806150222
398721UK00011B/688

9 781916 259454